"I'm not the same man I was, John."

"I'm not the same man," he countered easily. Too easily, Kelsey thought. She risked a glance at his face. His features were etched with unspoken emotion, but what emotions those might be, she couldn't begin to guess.

"I'm not married anymore," he added softly.

She smiled half-bitterly. "I'm not a victim anymore."

"I can see that," he said. He trailed the edge of his thumb along the curve of her cheek. A shiver followed in its wake, and goose bumps prickled on her arms. She wanted to tell him to go to hell and beg him to continue his touch all at the same time. She shifted her head away from that seductive contact.

"I wasn't kidding, John, when I said the Kelsey you knew was dead. I did die three years ago. And when I was born again, I had a new life, a new last name, and I found the only thing that really matters is anger."

Dear Reader:

We at Silhouette are very excited to bring you this reading Sensation. Look out for the four books which appear in our Silhouette Sensation series every month. These stories will have the high quality you have come to expect from Silhouette, and their varied and provocative plots will encourage you to explore the wonder of falling in love – again and again!

Emotions run high in these drama-filled novels. Greater sensual detail and an extra edge of realism intensify the hero and heroine's relationship so that you cannot help but be caught up in their every change of mood.

We hope you enjoy this Sensation – and will go on to enjoy many more.

We would love to hear your comments and encourage you to write to us:

Jane Nicholls
Silhouette Books
PO Box 236
Thornton Road
Croydon
Surrey
CR9 3RU

Extreme Justice
MARILYN TRACY

*First published in Great Britain in 1994
by Silhouette Books, Eton House, 18-24 Paradise Road,
Richmond, Surrey TW9 1SR*

© Tracy Le Cocq 1993

Silhouette, Silhouette Sensation and Colophon are
Trade Marks of Harlequin Enterprises B.V.

ISBN 0 373 59370 8

18-9412

Made and printed in Great Britain

Other novels by Marilyn Tracy

Silhouette Sensation

Too Good To Forget
No Place To Run

This book is dedicated to my parents,
Bob and Marilyn Huber,
for all their help.

Chapter 1

"**P**ack your bags, J.C., Winslow's out."

John Chandler didn't have to ask what his long-time friend and oftentimes partner was talking about. He muttered an obscenity.

"Your swearing days are just beginning, Johnny, boy. Pete, our man inside, says this bird is one unstable element. Apparently the entire time he's been in the hole he's gone out of orbit at least once a month. And always about Kelsey."

It seemed as if it was only yesterday that they had collared the lowlife and slipped him a one-way ticket to the Virginia State Penitentiary. Trouble was, the ticket hadn't been good for life, only for three years of concurrent time, and now the man was back on the streets, as dangerous a man as John Chandler had ever run across. And God knew, as an FBI agent, he'd run across his fair share.

"Is Kelsey still in the program?" John asked. He didn't think he stumbled over her name, was sure he hadn't, but that was how it felt.

Charlie Fulghum sighed and the phone crackled as if in protest. "If you can call it that now."

"Meaning?"

"Meaning she's a hard lady to keep under wraps."

"Where is she, Charlie?"

"You know the rules, no whereabouts over the phone. Besides, you're going to find out soon enough. You're the man assigned to her."

John didn't allow himself to think about the implications in that statement. Three years and he could still conjure her image as though he had her picture right in front of him. He thought instead of what Charlie had said earlier. "If she's in the program, why the assignment? How can Winslow find her?"

"Her face has been on TV almost as much as the national news broadcasters talking about her. I'm sure you've seen how the media's been rehashing her story every night at six and ten. Apparently, when the press got word of Winslow's parole, Kelsey became the number-one missing person. Her face has been shown on every channel and in every paper nationwide. And on one of those daytime phone-in talk shows a couple of days ago, somebody blabbed about not knowing her, but gave away the fact she was living in Texas, anyway."

"Damn," John said, but his mind was busy elsewhere, trying to fuse Kelsey Winslow with Texas. It wasn't working.

"And get this, this phone-in caller said our little Kelsey was teaching people how to protect themselves from 'Mr. Wrong.'"

John couldn't help but crack a slight smile. If anyone knew about Mr. Wrong, Kelsey did. But of all the rotten luck. Some busybody without anything better to do with their time, calling in, tipping Kelsey's hand . . . on national television no less.

The whole idea behind the Witness Protection Program was to keep witnesses or victims safe. And to do that, those same witnesses or victims had to keep a low profile. Thanks to the media, with their enthusiasm for keeping the public apprised of every detail of a criminal's life, and thanks to this anonymous busybody, Kelsey was right back where she was three years ago, in a whole heap of trouble.

"I suppose they gave a street address, too?"

"I guess we can thank the lady for small favors. The talk show's host managed to cut her off before she blurted out the city. But, hell, it won't take a genius to find her now."

"Let's hope he didn't see that show, then."

"Guess again, pal. He saw it."

"Speculating?"

"No such luck. He was twiddling his thumbs, waiting for the paperwork to be processed. Guards said he lit up like a Christmas tree when that stupid caller said her name, handed him the state of Texas on a silver platter."

"How long has he been out?"

"About thirty minutes now."

John looked at his watch. "Got a tail on him?"

"Sure. For all that means. Remember three years ago? The man could dodge us better than a fox running from hungry hounds."

John remembered all right.

"Our case worker handling Kelsey says our little gal has been saying some pretty harsh things about the justice system," Charlie said.

"Such as?"

"Such as the justice system wasn't in place to 'mete out justice but rather to study precedents, plea-bargain, and trade souls for political expediency.' She's been teaching other women how to save themselves. Are you ready for that?"

John couldn't be sure if it was the case worker saying all that, or if it really came from Kelsey. Whichever it was, he didn't blame Kelsey for being disillusioned. Three years ago her husband had hired a hit man to kill her, who would have succeeded if the man hadn't subcontracted the hit to undercover FBI agent Charlie Fulghum. And if the FBI, one John Chandler in particular, hadn't persuaded her to help them run a sting operation on Winslow.

The FBI and a very scared Kelsey Winslow—now Dobson—had executed an elaborate scheme to make her husband believe the hit had been carried out. They had faked her death, and then had proceeded to arrest Winslow when he'd met with his "hit man" to pay him for a job well-done. Unfortunately Kelsely's actually being alive and well had legally precluded sending her husband up on a murder charge. Doubly unfortunately, the federal judge had taken a dim view of their sting operation, saying that it had smacked of entrapment. And worst of all, the state judge hadn't liked the whole thing being dumped in his lap, so he'd issued a concurrent sentence instead of a consecutive sentence.

So Kelsey Winslow had been forced to sit through the trial, endure her husband's mealymouthed lies, his tears, and the realization that her life was, in judicial terms, worth a mere three years. Luckily John had managed to wrangle her a slot in the W.P.P. and she'd been whisked out of state, out of Winslow's reach.

If news hounds and a would-be do-gooder had kept her *off* television, that would still have been the case.

And now, apparently, he was assigned to safeguard her again.

"You got the tail. I assume we're already watching her house. So why me?" John asked, as much of himself as of Charlie.

"You know her. Technically she's still in the program. We can't have strangers knocking on her door and saying they're Bureau. A couple of bucks and any local library will laminate a badge for somebody. She'll need to see someone she knows.''

''Why not you? Or Jackson? You two are the Bureau's top hot dogs.''

''Says you. But the chief says only the best for this one,'' Charlie said. ''Shows what little he knows. Besides, Jackson's still in the hospital from that little car chase last month—'' he broke off to fill John in on his prognosis, which was fairly good ''—and I'm undercover again, Johnny, boy.''

''Who are you this time?''

''Not who, *what*. I'm a rich yuppie gone haywire, flying back and forth to Peru to watch flying saucers.''

''Much crime in that? Or are you trying to hitch a lift to another planet?'' John's mind wasn't on Charlie's operation, but rather on a tear-streaked face that for some reason wasn't a whit blurred with time.

''It's amazing how much cocaine these close encounters produce.''

''Working with Treasury on this?''

''Sure. Look, if you want your chart done, I can get you a good deal. And, if you want to trade cases, I'll do it in a New York minute.''

''If you can guarantee that Kelsey isn't going to slam the door in my face when I go a-knocking, then by all means, go for it.''

''Just try for a little charm, Chandler. It's a five-letter word.''

''What's it mean?''

''Look it up. While you're at it, you might cross-reference 'tact.' ''

''I'm in the Bureau, not diplomacy,'' John said. ''My job description says carry a badge, not flowers.''

''Beats me why you got women chasing after you, Chandler. According to the latest magazines, women like a little razzle-dazzle now and then. A lady who gives lectures about Mr. Wrong might be more easily approached through those channels.''

''You learned how to read on your last assignment, did you? Anybody call Ripley's?''

John was glad the chief had handed Charlie the task of bringing him into this case. The easy banter they'd always maintained and their long-standing relationship allowed him to read between the lines. The primary unspoken message was: *Kelsey's different.* The chief wouldn't have passed this along. How was she different? She was talking about Mr. Wrong, for one thing. That right there showed a pretty big change from the nervous, fragile woman he'd known three years ago.

John asked for some details—the wheres, whens and hows—and Charlie told him a packet would be arriving for him shortly. They gave each other a few casual verbal punches and hung up. But John didn't move away from the phone for a few minutes. His mind chased stray thoughts around in his head like a dog chased its own mangy tail.

What would Kelsey have to say to a bunch of victims about protecting themselves from Mr. Wrong? She had been about as capable of defending herself as a kitten would have been at avoiding a pack of hungry coyotes. He could all too easily remember her sweetly rounded, trembling form securely wrapped in his arms.

That memory was too much; now he *had* to move. He shoved away from the desk. He'd only been back in D.C. for a couple of weeks and the mountain of paperwork had already been whittled down to creditable size. As usual, he'd turned the stack upside down and worked in that fashion, from the bottom up, past to most recent. He only had last week's files left to log. He could be ready to leave in fifteen minutes.

The thought that he'd been back in D.C. only a few days and would be leaving again so quickly didn't bother him. That was his job. The ability to hop a plane at any hour, to sky out, resolve a case and depart as quickly was part of the reason he, Charlie and Jackson were three of the most traveled agents in the Bureau and why they served as a three-member trouble-shooter team that bounced around the country almost as often as airline pilots.

The fact that this jumping around the continent had cost both Charlie and John their marriages, and made Jackson a hardened bachelor, scarcely even crossed John's mind anymore. Not having a particular district, not being tied down to administrative duties, lent each assignment an element of adventure, sometimes even danger. Even the lousy hold-somebody's-hand assignments took on a different cast when the locale was different, the case fresh.

Each of the three men was uniquely suited to the strange life-style. Charlie and Jackson had both come from traveling backgrounds, had fathers who were roving salesmen and who had taken their families with them from locale to locale. Those two had grown up in twenty or thirty different states, dozens of different schools, never having any real roots or place to call home.

As an environmental opposite, John had been raised in a small-town church home for orphans in Montana, had never strayed more than four miles from the old building with its population of thirty kids who'd grown up never knowing the meaning of love and trust. Unlike many of the kids in the home, John hadn't been an orphan, his parents were alive and presumably well somewhere, anywhere but with him. He'd had relatives, too, but they couldn't be bothered with an extra mouth to feed. John didn't feel any animosity toward them; it was a matter of hard reality in hard times.

As a youngster, John's only ambition had been to get as far away from Montana as he possibly could. The army was the quickest ticket out. And the army had suited John right down to his toenails. And luckily for him, one of his commanding officers had seen something special in the young, restive private assigned to his platoon. He had encouraged John to stick out the army for a few more years and let them pick up the tab for a college education. Criminal justice had claimed his attention, not the prosecuting-defending end of justice, but the face-to-face-confrontation-with-the-criminal-element kind of justice.

The Bureau had offered him a job when he'd graduated and, after he'd repaid the college debt by serving another four years—this time as an officer himself—he'd signed on with the FBI. He was now approaching forty, and eligible for retirement in another seven years if he didn't fold in his army time, next year if he did. But John had no intention of quitting the Bureau; it was his life.

John sighed, stretching his back, hands on those particular muscles that sometimes refused to cooperate no matter how many sit-ups he managed in the morning. A bullet nearly four years ago had ripped right through him. Maybe that's why his back seemed to hurt now, because he was going to see Kelsey Winslow again. His damaged back had been the whole reason he'd been assigned to her case in the first place. It was supposed to have been a cushy job.

Damn, he murmured, not directing the remark at anything in particular. Circumstance, perhaps, or maybe the vagaries of memory. That particular assignment had been anything but easy and for a host of reasons that had nothing at all to do with danger, the Bureau, or Bill Winslow's sociopathic tendencies.

Three years had passed since then. Three long, event-filled years. Time that had nothing to do with Kelsey Winslow's blue eyes, shaking, delicate fingers, or silky blond hair. Certainly time enough for her face to have blurred with a hundred other faces, for her case to have been lost in the complex filing system in his head. But, no, here was that file, right on top, right where he had shoved it on a December morning three years earlier.

How many times had he taken that particular mental file out and reviewed it? More than he ever would have admitted aloud. And each time he had remembered a single stolen kiss, and that look of hurt in her eyes when he'd told her he had to leave, that the case was finished. Have a good life.

This was *his* mental file, so it seemed unfair that he couldn't switch a few details, alter a fact here and there, and close it once and for all, store it back in the dark corners that held all the other closed cases, memories too uncomfortable to review, chapters ended. What was it about Kelsey that seemed to defy being shut away in the dusty recesses of his mind? What was it about the memory of her that wouldn't let him forget her?

Wednesday, November 10
1:00 p.m., Leesburg, Virginia

Bill Winslow leaned back from the café's chipped Formica countertop and lit a cigarette. He pushed his nearly polished plate to one side to use as an ashtray though there was one within reach. He slowly swung around on the barstool, surveying the other occupants of the small backwoods Virginia eatery. One was a local farmer, judging by his dirt-encrusted coveralls and faded flannel shirt. Another was a long-haired, scruffy man of about thirty in an army flak jacket who continually made passes at his nose with a tissue, all while studying what looked to be the want ads in the local paper. The third and final diner in the café, excluding the rather scrawny waitress with the chipped nail polish, was dressed in suit and tie, and reading a Virginia state map as though it were a Harvard classic.

Bill smiled. He paid his check before finishing his cigarette and didn't leave a tip. He'd learned early in life that you only tip when you're going to come back to a place and wanted something from the waiter or waitress. This one he would never see again, so there wasn't anything she would ever be doing for him, ergo, no extra change was necessary. He strolled out into the sunshine and turned up his jacket collar against the chill wind. For a moment he just stood there, his face to the sun, as though he had all the time in the world, as if he were savoring the enjoyment of his new-found freedom.

As he expected, the businessman came out of the café, fumbled with his keys and climbed into a Chevy that had seen better days but was freshly waxed. Bill watched him set the map aside and put the car in gear. He raised a hand as the driver slowly pulled out of the parking slot. The driver stopped and rolled down his window.

"Are you heading into the woods country?" he asked with a slight smile.

"How did you know that?" the driver asked.

"I saw you reading the map," Bill supplied, his smile broadening. "Salesman?"

"That's right," the man said. He gestured with his thumb toward the trunk of the car. "Got a bunch of medical supplies my company's trying to peddle to the smaller clinics."

"I'm heading to Berkeley Springs, and I know the back roads pretty well," Bill said. "I don't suppose you'd like a guide?"

The driver hesitated a moment, then nodded at the passenger door.

Bill walked around the car, relaxed and easy. He climbed in the seat, pulled the door shut behind him. As they were driving away he glanced in the side mirror in time to see the scruffy young man emerge from the café, his nose no longer dripping, his newspaper apparently forgotten, a frown creasing his brow.

Bill smiled and introduced himself to his mark. The game had begun.

Wednesday, November 10
1:30 p.m., Washington, D.C.

One of the office assistants pushed through the door, a huge stack of files in her arms, obscuring her face. She walked by John's desk and, without pausing, tossed the thick envelope in her hand in the general direction of his chair. He caught it and was about to throw back some wisecrack when he saw the name across the envelope, Kelsey Winslow/Dobson.

He sat back down, forgetting all about perky, hardworking Annie and her stack of files. This was the one that interested him. The only one. He unwound the string binding the seal and dumped the contents on his desk. Naturally the top item was a photograph of Kelsey. It figured.

She was even pretty in black and white. All soft curves and sharp contrasts. He flipped the photo over and saw that it had been taken almost three years earlier. Was that why it seemed that fear and hurt still lingered in her gaze? Were those emotions still there now or would he be the one to reawaken that particular haunted expression?

He set the photo aside, deliberately turning it facedown. Attraction didn't have a place in responding to a case. He picked up the next sheet of paper. A memorandum of conversation from their man inside the pen. John couldn't help but feel a pang of pity for Pete Dahlstrom. That poor guy switched prison cells more often than most hardened criminals. John didn't think any amount of bonus cash would compensate for that kind of detail. But Pete claimed to like the routines, like the danger element. He also liked his paid-for Jaguar and house in the Seychelles.

According to Pete's notes, most of which corroborated what Charlie had said on the phone, Winslow was definitely a candidate for the nearest shrink's couch. But for all his outbursts, he hadn't been involved in any prison unrest and had somehow pulled down a good-behavior rap. Nuts, but polite was the overall review. But in Pete's notes an ominous thread recurred. Winslow certainly hadn't forgotten Kelsey, the scam she'd helped perpetrate on him, and most particularly, her testimony against him in court. Agents inside had managed to get their hands on a diary of sorts when

Winslow was transferred from one cell to another wing a couple of months back. It, too, was included in the packet, a note from Pete attached.

According to the attachment, each of Winslow's "outbursts" coincided with the diatribes to be found inside the diary, and all of those focused on what Winslow planned to do to Kelsey upon his release. And each of them cursed the FBI for hiding her whereabouts from him.

Another item in the packet was a review of Winslow's release, complete with the guard's comments on the prisoner's reaction to the television show mentioning Kelsey. Also enclosed was a video tape of the program. John smiled wryly as he crossed the room to the television set and plugged the tape into a VCR slot, depressing the Play button; the Bureau was nothing if not efficient.

The television screen lit up and revealed the opening sequence of a popular daytime talk show. The host, a pretty, petite blonde, told her audience to take out pens and pads, they were all going to learn how to cushion their lives to avoid the kind of man like Bill Winslow, the man stirring up all the controversy these days because he was being released after three years' prison time after having been found guilty of hiring a man to kill his wife. The host said that no one knew the whereabouts of Kelsey Winslow, but that everyone there sincerely hoped all was well with her.

She went on to say that with them that day were panelists from all parts of the country, each working in different ways to help women avoid the pitfalls of placing their trust in the wrong man. The panelists ranged from a woman who ran an underground railroad system to aid women in recovering their kidnapped children, to a male attorney who had just written a book on the legal issues involved in suing a parent for child abuse that occurred more than twenty years ago.

John was fairly impressed with how knowledgeable these panelists were, even found himself nodding his head at some of the advice the underground railroad woman was giving, and this despite the fact that he didn't agree with going around the law. But however much he worked to uphold the system, he had to admit that it failed some people—these women whose children's purportedly abusive fathers had been granted custody or had kidnapped the children, or people such as Kelsey, who had to face her murderous ex-husband's "good behaviour" release.

The show, for all its information, was largely innocuous, and certainly couldn't have hurt anyone, until the phone-in part came up. Whatever had been said by the panelists was largely ignored by the callers, each of whom seemed to have some personal ax to grind. "My husband left me five years ago for a younger woman...what should I do? She shouldn't be entitled to his retirement, should she? I was the one who raised his two children, who had to live with him for thirty years." There were other callers like that one, some advising, some nearly begging. The host handled them all graciously and smoothly.

And then it came. The camera was panning the audience, the panelists, the host. A woman's voice asked if the host could hear her. At the affirmative, the voice congratulated the panelists on their help to women who had had difficulties. "I know how valuable that is," she said. "I mean, I've been there. And I'll tell you something, I really feel sorry for Kelsey Winslow having to run from her ex-husband. I know a woman here in Texas who looks a lot like her—in fact, it's amazing, they even have the same first name...Kelsey, and I mean to tell you, it made me wonder, they look like identical *twins*—but anyway, this woman I know isn't a victim. I mean, she's *strong*.

"And she learned it all herself. Taught herself, I mean. And she's sharing that with other people. People like me. She's taught me *so* much. I'll never be a victim again. She's got a different name now, and she's very strong. She teaches all kinds of women not to be afraid anymore. I mean, she's got her life together. Kelsey, my Kelsey, I mean, isn't scared anymore.''

John groaned as the camera did a close-up shot of first the show's host and then the lawyer on stage. Both of them wore the same expression of shocked enlightenment. John was sure that same look was on his own face.

This was more than a would-be do-gooder. This woman was a menace to the human race. If she *had* given Kelsey's address, she could hardly have made it any clearer that Kelsey Winslow was alive and well in Texas. It was a big state, but Winslow was a bigger nut. The camera again focused on the host who was calmly thanking the caller. John could have kissed the woman when she offered the placid suggestion that Kelsey Winslow would be glad to know that someone was fighting back, that wherever she might be, it would probably make her happy to know that a namesake was making it possible for other women to avoid what she'd gone through. She closed the program with a thanks to the panelists and offered the microphone to a member of the audience as the credits rolled.

But no matter how smoothly she'd handled the call, the damage had been done. John's first course of action would be to contact the station to make certain the FBI had already slapped a suppression on their phone records so that Winslow couldn't trace the location of that ridiculous call. He was on the phone to the show's producer before the credits even finished rolling.

As luck would have it, he was patched into the host herself, and after a terse explanation of what he needed, she immediately assured him of her program's compliance. She wished him luck, took down the Bureau's Texas number so she could report any requests that might come in, and hung up.

With an angry jab, John ejected the tape. Whoever that caller was, she was a bloody idiot. And right now, he projected that anger to Kelsey for teaching survival techniques to such jerkwater women as the one who had called in. What was she thinking of, being so public? He'd busted his fanny to get her into the Witness Protection Program, pulling every string he could to get her safe, all because he'd believed what she'd told him about her ex-husband. And then she had to go and amass the kind of dippy fans who called in on national television shows and all but spelled out her whereabouts to the world at large.

John tossed the tape on the desk and picked up the rest of the chief's information sheets. The guards had reported that Winslow had hardly seemed to react to hearing Kelsey's name mentioned, that he'd only grinned. Broadly. But what he'd said—and what he'd written in his diary—had made the guards slip the word to Pete, who had immediately called the Bureau.

If you want something done right, you know you just got to do it yourself. That was all Winslow had said, and looking at the words, John knew he shouldn't have felt a cold chill work up his arms. But the guards—and Pete backed this up—said in the notes that it wasn't the words that got to them. "It was the look in the guy's eyes. Glittery. Like a wolverine's. Spooky."

Of all the animals, the wolverine was the most dangerous, because it was the only one that killed for the sheer sake of slaughter. John had to wonder how a wolverine could be released on good behavior.

Yet Bill Winslow had been released, set back into the world, free to become a member of society, debts paid, penance served. Three years in a federal prison done, spent, and well finished.

If you want something done right . . .

There was really only one way to interpret that remark. Winslow had been angry enough, possessive enough and undeniably enough of a nut case to hire a killer for his wife three years ago simply because she'd been trying to get free of him through the divorce-court system. Now, after public humiliation, three years in prison, loss of home, business *and* wife, it didn't take a mastermind to understand that he'd be more than a little upset. And that he fully intended to finish the job he'd started three years ago. But this time, he was going to do it himself.

John opened the diary, flipped a few pages, scanning them swiftly, looking for any indication that Winslow might have known Kelsey's whereabouts. What he read convinced him it was a damn good thing the man hadn't known where she was. She wouldn't have been alive to be talked about by that caller. She might know a lot about Mr. Wrong, but Winslow was a step beyond "wrong"; he was well on his way to berserk.

The vitriol, the viciousness and the sheer bizarre quality of Winslow's entries made John's stomach knot in hot anger, his jaw clench in disgust. A man such as this could get off on good behavior? No wonder society was so screwed up, he thought. Something like this, a man such as Winslow, created a whole world of confusion around the fuzzy concept of "good" and "bad." This man wasn't just *bad,* he was crazy bad.

John dropped the diary to the desk as though it soiled his hands. He almost shoved it into the trash can, but knew he couldn't. It definitely could be used as evidence against Winslow. Could be used as proof he intended his former wife some amazing forms of torture. John flipped it into the packet, scarcely touching it.

Frowning heavily now, he sorted through the rest of the paperwork for the one thing he sought. He scooped it up with an almost angry swipe. Flicking open the narrow flap, he checked the departure schedule and the airline he would be traveling. And, most important, the destination.

Lubbock, Texas. Why did that still strike him as unlikely? Because he pictured her in the smallish, redbrick Colonial outside Bethesda, Maryland? Or was it because something about the expansive skies and broad, flat terrain that surrounded Lubbock seemed too big for Kelsey, too frightening for an Eastern city girl who had already been too harshly used? Did she like it there? Did she miss the lush greenery of Maryland?

John had been in Lubbock only once, and that for a congressional delegation assignment that had meant four days in hotel rooms eating room service overcooked steaks and trying not to think about his marriage that had finally and irrevocably bitten the proverbial dust. Dayna had cried when she'd told him it was over; he could still remember that. And she'd said, an odd note of sadness in her voice, that she hoped he'd meet someone who broke his heart one day... because then at least she'd know he had one.

Had Kelsey been in Lubbock, then? He wished he'd known, and, at the same time, was glad that he hadn't. For if he *had* known she was there, he might have given in to temptation and called, done the ordinary ask-her-out-to-dinner, talk-about-old-times routine. Only he would have been going against company rules. And he would have left town a couple of days later without having changed anyway, still the rolling stone that never got close enough to anything to gather the moss that cluttered life.

The notion of arriving in Lubbock now, only to ride off again into that age-old sunset, having presumably saved the day and won the battle but ultimately feeling he might yet again be losing some war he didn't even want to understand, made him feel inexpressibly lonely.

He stuffed the packet contents back into the Kelsey-marked envelope, called a goodbye to his co-workers—most of whom were practically strangers as he so seldom saw them—and was out the side door of the main Bureau. He was across Dupont Circle in a matter of minutes and in his place off Connecticut Avenue in even less.

Inside his nearly austere apartment, and for the first time since the call had come in about Winslow, John relaxed

somewhat. Once again, he was donning the white hat, setting out to vanquish the bad guys. He knew his role, he was
the faceless stranger who never got involved, let nothing interfere with his job, with the task at hand. Yes, he knew his
job well, did it even better and could rely upon his instincts
for survival. And as always, he'd leave, heart whole and
ready for the next challenge.

He felt ready. Prepared. Ready to see Kelsey Winslow
again. His smile faded. He felt strangely irritated. Not angry, exactly, just out of sorts, a feeling that seemed to inter-
sect somewhere between anticipation and extreme
reluctance. Unbidden, the memory of that single kiss he'd
shared with Kelsey Winslow crept into his mind.

It had happened the night of her "reported" death. She'd
been standing in her tidy little kitchen, filling something—
a glass of water, or the coffeepot, he couldn't remember
which—at the sink. She'd been unaware he was standing in
the doorway, leaning against the jamb. He hadn't been
talking, hadn't been even really thinking, just watching her.
She'd been the picture of courage during the whole soiree.
But just then, when she didn't know anyone was watching
her, when she'd thought she was all alone, doing some routine task, her blond hair caught up in a loose half braid at
the back of her neck, he'd seen her shoulders heave, had
seen her whole body tremble in a shudder that seemed to
come more from her soul than from any physical plane.

She'd dropped whatever it was she'd been filling. It had
clattered like an alarm in the sink. If he'd been smart, he'd
have listened to the message in that sharp sound, he'd have
turned around and left the room, left her to her tears, given
her the privacy she probably needed.

But he hadn't abandoned her to the grief that rocked her.
He hadn't even thought about it. He'd crossed the small
kitchen in less time than it takes to tell and had pulled her
into his arms. He'd told himself then—tried reminding
himself now—that he'd intended it as comfort only. Just a

shoulder to cry on. Just acting the role of that nameless, faceless knight who saved the damsels in distress in all the stories with the sunset endings.

But with her trembling body against his, her warm face pressed to his collarbone, her silken hair brushing his face, he'd found himself forgetting she was running for her life, that he was married, that he never *ever* got involved. When she'd turned her face upward, her blue eyes shimmering with tears, her lips parted with unspoken question, unvoiced need, he'd succumbed to an irresistible urge to taste her.

And was immediately sorry for he felt he was drowning in the promise of her lips, the pliant body against his, the need, the want that threatened to engulf them both. He'd felt her tremble then, but for a different reason than when he'd crossed the room. He'd recognized the difference because he'd felt the echo reverberating in him.

And three years later, a million people and miles between them, he still remembered it. Still felt the distant resonance that she'd sparked in him. And he remembered how he'd pulled away, holding her at full arm's length, still feeling the electricity that sparked between them despite the distance, in spite of his determination *not* to feel it. Her eyes had been half-closed, he remembered, her lips full and moist, dewy... kissed. Her lower lip had quivered, as though begging for more, and her breath had been ragged. God. No man had ever been offered such an enticing invitation, and nothing had been more difficult than walking away from it.

"I'm married," he'd said. Even as he'd said it, he wondered why he'd told her. He told himself then, and tried believing it again now, that he'd done so because he was a man who played by the rules, who lived by them, who made his living upholding them; it was all he knew and all he believed in. But there was more to his two words than that. He'd known it then, still couldn't deny it now.

In that single kiss, in the feel of her in his arms, the want of her in his body, the taste of her on his lips, Kelsey Winslow had ceased to be a "case"—she'd become a threat. Certainly not to his marriage, that had been as over as anything, but the final decree could make it even then. No, it was a lot more dangerous to *him,* to the barriers he'd placed between himself and the world long ago. And that was a threat he would not allow.

Looking at him with large, hurt eyes, a rigidity stealing into the shoulders that only seconds before had been malleable and fluid, Kelsey Winslow had suddenly become everything that John Chandler had avoided like the very plague. She had represented involvement with a capital *I.*

And big, brave John Chandler had run away as hard and as fast as he possibly could. Oh, he'd finished the job, he'd bagged the bad guy, made sure Winslow was sent up, had even arranged for Kelsey to be squeezed into the Witness Protection Program, telling himself he could do no more for her than that, ensuring her safety for life.

But he'd been running the whole time. He'd hidden behind the mask of duty, responsibility and nobility until all those virtues tasted like yesterday's soured milk.

And here he was again, packing to wing his way to rescue Kelsey Winslow. He was finished in less than fifteen minutes. It was as if he'd practiced this drill at least once a week every week for the time Winslow had been in jail. True, he was continually on the road, used to having to pack rapidly. But now, the whole time he was tossing spare clothes, shaving kit and that packet of potential evidence into the canvas overnight bag, adding a few Bureau items like a phone scrambler, a slim, laptop computer with a patch-in system and a couple of other handy doodads, he found himself thinking about a pair of eyes that sparkled when they were amused, a set of lips that seemed as generous as a summer's morning, tears that spilled hot and salty, cleansing her soul but searing his. ...e could try to kid himself until the proverbial cows came home but this wasn't just a case. It was *Kelsey's* case.

The four words rattled around in John's mind like a marble in a tin can, ricocheting back and forth, echoes of a nightmare that should have ended three years ago, but which, instead, had merely been put in temporary abeyance. Out of nowhere came the notion that it was time to pay the piper. Winslow's time? Kelsey's? Or was it his, John's, time to finish off things never really started?

He thought about Charlie's unspoken message of Kelsey's being different. There were such things as surface changes, but Charlie's tone had implied other alterations. If Kelsey was teaching women how to peg a Mr. Wrong, had she found his counterpart, Mr. Right?

If she was speaking in public, standing up for women's rights, disguised or not, then she had changed, indeed. Because three years ago, Kelsey hadn't stood a prayer against Winslow. Delicate, fragile, blue eyes as big as twin skies, full lips pressed together to hide their trembling, and already frazzled by the decision to divorce, the bitterness and physical abuse she'd suffered in that trying period had made her understandably confused and frightened when John and his team of agents had appeared on her doorstep with the news of the contract her husband had put out on her. And she'd been further frightened by their scheme to not only save her life, but to put her husband away, as well.

Scared or not, Kelsey had performed her role exactly as they had commanded, had never even questioned their dictates, had, in fact, allowed them to take over her life and her subsequent "death" with an equanimity that spoke of her innate courage rather than any degree of fear. This was no small endeavor on her part, she had had to allow friends and family to believe she was dead. She'd had to listen to accounts of her own memorial service. She'd had to hold herself off from everything she'd ever known, place her fate in

the hands of strangers. Yet something in her character, her
basic integrity, had carried her through the whole trau-
matic time.

And for John that glimpse into Kelsey's personality during those two months had been like a peek into another
universe. He had never met anyone like her, probably never
would again. She had seemed like everything decent, honest and trustworthy that the world could possibly offer. Instead of hysterics at finding four FBI agents in her living
room, talking about a contract on her life, she'd calmly
made them coffee. She'd even set out a tray of homemade
cookies for them to munch on while they described her
husband's hiring of a hit man to end her life.

Rather than making John feel that she wasn't bright
enough to grasp that her bad-news husband was trying to
kill her, for God's sake—as Charlie had even whispered to
John through a mouthful of chocolate-chip cookie—John
had instinctively known that the coffee, the cookies, the
primly folded hands over crossed elegant legs were the actions of a woman who needed something to do, some kind
of activity to mask the roiling fear inside her.

Later, when he knew her better, he'd seen the telltale signs
of her fear more clearly, the myriad small details that gave
her nervousness away. Polishing the counter when she'd
done it only moments before, brewing another pot of coffee before the first one was even drained, preparing elaborate meals for the men camped out in her home; she'd done
them all, and all were masks. But occasionally she'd meet his
eyes and her guard would fall abruptly and he'd see the host
of terrors she'd been forced to suffer in the past, the horror
and embarrassment she was feeling then. And he had
longed, in sour vain, to take her into his arms and kiss away
the pain, the fear, give her all the solace and wonder of a
distraction. And something more than a distraction. He'd
wanted, with everything in him, to erase that studious
courage. And the one time he had given in to that urge, that

irresistible demand, he'd been the one to pull back, to say no to her unvoiced plea.

And as a result of that kiss, that mistake, he hadn't allowed himself to do more than merely stand beside her through the dark days of transition. She was a case, nothing more. A job. And he was married. No matter how poorly that marriage was faring, he'd told himself he was still wholly committed to it. He smiled bitterly now, remembering to whom that commitment had been. Dayna, who wished he would meet someone who would break his heart.

He half suspected that if he'd hung around Kelsey Winslow any longer than was absolutely necessary, Dayna might well have gotten her wish.

John still remembered reading the account of her "death" in the newspapers. In an area where violence was daily fare, her story still made juicy stuff and it had played across the front pages like the circulars of the circus coming to town. According to the reports, Kelsey's Mercury had been found abandoned on a back road outside Berkeley Springs, Virginia, Type-B positive blood found on the seat, the wheel and in various locations outside the vehicle. While Kelsey Winslow's body hadn't been recovered, police had found a torn and bloody tennis shoe of the size and style worn by the missing woman some distance from the car. Her grieving husband, nearly hysterical at the news of the car's recovery, had reported her missing days earlier. His distraught account of their blissful marriage brought floods of sympathy letters pouring into newspapers. He cried on television. But the final accounts stated that though the search for Kelsey would be continuing, the police held little hope for her being found alive.

The picture of the blood-drenched tennis shoe had lodged in John's mind like a grappling hook into sandstone. And even though Kelsey had been sitting right beside him while he studied that photograph, and later when they saw it on television, always close enough to feel her body heat, smell the light scent of her clean, lemony perfume, he'd had the gut-wrenching feeling that he was reading, seeing, the real thing. He'd staged the whole shebang—except for that godawful tennis shoe; that had been Charlie's invention—but had still suffered the gnawing feeling they were tempting fate.

He still felt that way. He could understand the superstitious orphanage warden who had often said, "Never lie about someone lest you make it come true. Never taunt fate lest you want that fate to be yours." She had been right, that cold, wise and oftentimes cruel warden. They had tempted fate, taunted it, lying as they had about Kelsey's death.

But the lie had proved effective. Bill Winslow had driven to Virginia, and in the lounge of a sleazy motel, met the FBI ringer, Charlie Fulghum, and coolly pulled out ten thousand dollars of pure blood money. He hadn't been so cool when a host of FBI agents stepped out of the shadows and collared him while Charlie traded him a pair of handcuffs for the money. He'd gone off in an elaborate tirade of real estate deals and would-be shopping centers. He'd all but sobbed that it was all a mistake, they had him all wrong. The first guy he'd talked to had totally misunderstood. And he'd been oh, so innocent, so injured during his trial. Until he'd seen Kelsey walk in the courtroom escorted by John and Charlie. He hadn't been cool then.

John glanced at his watch and saw that despite his roller-coaster ride down memory lane, it had only been an hour since Charlie called to let him know Winslow was out and Chandler was back on the case.

It wasn't until he was actually on the road, speeding toward Washington, D.C.'s National Airport, that he allowed himself to open that mental file again, remember Kelsey as she had been. But he fought the memory of that one kiss they'd shared, that one glimpse of a different future, an alternate reality. He had never really forgotten that kiss, it hadn't been possible. But he had to shove it down, lock it up and throw out the key, because it would only interfere with duty, only get in the way of things he had to do.

Because if he fully studied that moment, held it up to the harsh light of a three-year, long-delayed scrutiny, he would have to remember her parting words. In that harsh light, the words trailed the memory of the kiss like night following day, like tears following pain.

"Thanks for everything, Agent Chandler. You'll forgive me if I don't keep in touch."

Her rich, soft voice had broken on the last word.

He swore as he swung the overnighter from the car.

Chapter 2

Kelsey typed steadily, unaware of the shadows creeping across the terra-cotta-colored, Saltillo-tiled floor and up the creamy stucco walls beside her. She saw only the words on the computer's amber screen, hearing only the same questions asked over and over at every support meeting after each seminar. She had some answers, and she'd given them out like candies tossed from a float during a Fourth of July parade. Some were taken to heart while more were left to melt on the hot Lubbock asphalt streets, unheeded, untaken.

She sat back, scrolling the screen to the beginning of the document, wishing she didn't feel so angry, hoping that this time she could read the tips, see the information without that constant companion of rage. But this time was no different.

Recognizing Mr. Wrong.

She pressed the delete button and eradicated the gerund. Now it read, simply, *Mr. Wrong*. She sighed. She wasn't a writer. Never would be. But she wanted a basic handout for the seminars she gave, for the workshops, even for the Monday-night support-group meetings. Maybe it wasn't so much how it was worded that was important, but rather what it had to say.

She reviewed the elementary list of how to spot a potential Mr. Wrong. She moved a couple of the items to the Secondary Warning Signals list, and reviewed the list again. She'd only left ten danger signals on the screen. That was enough. More, and people wouldn't listen, less and they would spend all their time trying to come up with more.

She read aloud. "Number one, he is reluctant to give you a home or office phone number." She wondered if she should elaborate now, or wait to do that until the text portion of her handout. She decided to wait.

It was odd that something so basic should have to be cited on a list. But she hadn't known. Hadn't wanted to know, perhaps.

She continued. "Number two, he is vague about his address." She felt the sneer of self-contempt curve her lips. Longer ago than she cared to remember, Bill had told her that he had just moved to town and didn't really have a permanent address yet. But he'd had no address at all. He'd been living out of his car and his former girlfriend's place until he'd roped Kelsey in.

"Number three, he uses the telephone all the time and hangs up swiftly when you enter the room." She thought about splitting this into two different "Mr. Wrong" tips, but shrugged and left it as one. Either way, the message was a bad one. Using the telephone incessantly was a sure indicator of insecurity if nothing more; hanging up when someone else entered the room could either indicate an affair or some "deal" going down. And a reluctance to talk about the call only underscored the inappropriate behavior in any case.

She pushed away from the computer, suddenly too angry to continue editing her list. These seemed like a first-grader's etiquette rules. Number one should read: When he hires a hit man to kill you, you can be fairly certain you've hooked up with the wrong man.

When would it go away, this feeling of having been used, taken and then abused? Bill had been sent to prison. He was locked up. Gone. And she'd been robbed of her life and shunted off to the far ends of the earth to keep her safe from his wrath.

Surely three years was too long to carry this degree of anger inside her. But it was the very anger that sustained her, that allowed her to sit over a computer, like today, trying to capsulize the essence of her seminars on avoiding the Bill Winslows of the world.

And it was the anger in her that had allowed her to recognize Lubbock, Texas, for what it was: a second chance. It was a thriving, vital community that demanded she swim or sink in the dust that occasionally swept in from the plains, a grim reminder of the desert lying only a few miles outside of that bright oasis.

She had huddled inside a high-rise apartment for the first several months, regretting the past, fearful of the present and future, afraid of Lubbock, the friendly people, the store clerks who seemed to always want to chat or offer a piece of advice. She'd been frightened of her new last name, afraid she would hesitate over it, or spell it wrong. She'd been afraid of the big skies, the dramatic thunderstorms, frightened of anything and anyone.

And one day she'd woken up and donned the same ratty housecoat, shuffled through the same undecorated, uninspiring apartment and stopped in front of the bathroom medicine cabinet mirror. She had stared at her unwashed face, her long, unstyled, uncombed hair in that twelve-by-twelve-inch square of glass, and had felt the same panic she'd suffered every day since finding out Bill wanted her dead. At that precise moment something inside had snapped.

Ever since that day, she'd striven to be a different Kelsey, a stronger version of herself, a Kelsey who would never be a victim again, would never be the kind of dupe that Bill Winslow had drawn in and then, when he'd used her all up, reduced her self-esteem to rubble, decided to kill her just because he couldn't bear to see her leave him, or worse, because she simply stood in his way. That was the final insult of all insults, that all she'd represented was some kind of obstacle, a kink in his plans.

The new Kelsey had been born that morning.

She smiled now, the bittersweet memory tugging at her. That old Kelsey seemed like such a stranger. The housecoat, the apartment, the tangled blond hair, the nightmares, they were all things of the past. She'd found a house in the suburban district of Lubbock within that week, bought it on a two-party real estate contract—so she didn't have to deal with credit history—with less than a thousand dollars down, sold it a year later for a healthy profit and used the cash for a down payment on her present home, taking a second mortgage on it to finance her small home business. She'd enrolled in martial arts classes, weapons training, and had started attending support-group meetings for abused women.

She'd found a life, had carved one out of virtually nothing, and was now fully and wholly Kelsey Dobson, self-made woman.

Yet, now, three long years after her escape from Bill, after her hard work at her new life, she could still be hurt, could still feel angry over the memory of what Bill had put her through, of what she'd foolishly walked right into, guard down, arms open wide. And worst of all, judging by her suddenly trembling fingers, she still wasn't immune to Bill's presence on this earth.

She drew a couple of deep, steadying breaths, let the last one seep into her, held it tight and still before releasing it, as though, by the simple act of breathing out, she was letting go of all the bad feelings Bill inspired in her. It was good therapy and better practice. Unfortunately, as now, it didn't always work. She slid open a sliding glass panel and went outside her back patio doors onto the broad southwestern veranda, tiled with the same tile as the interior of the house only rougher, not polished. It was an extension of the room, not quite outdoors, open to the elements but protective, as well.

The sharp scent of pine burning in someone's fireplace stung her nostrils and she realized for the first time that it was late in the afternoon, nearly nightfall. And it was winter, though it didn't look it, didn't particularly feel like it. The temperature was a mild fifty degrees and the sky was clear and seemed to stretch upward and outward into a mauve-shaded infinity.

Her automatic yard lights were already on, the little electric tiki torches giving off a party atmosphere. The stillness of the evening, the torches, the richness of the lawn, still green and taking water, stretching some forty yards to the evergreen honeysuckle vines that draped over the high cinder block wall, made her feel oddly peaceful and restless simultaneously.

Anything as large and elegant as that lawn needed sharing, and she had no one to share it with outside her support group and the selected few students she trained at home.

Could she have evening workshops? she wondered, taking in the lines of her yard, the privacy, the almost sanctuary feel of the place. Maybe. But she didn't much desire to have people around the place after dark. No particular reason, she lied to herself, just that she could never be quite certain someone hadn't messed with her gate locks, or left one of the gates open.

But she could use the money. A voice inside her added, *And the company. You could sure use the company.* It was difficult to start life over completely at thirty-three. She was trying to do everything alone, constantly aware of the balance in her checking account, continually afraid she would make an error in judgment over a seminar, a workshop idea. Then, as if by dark and evil magic, her fledgling business would simply vanish, her mortgage would balloon and her hope of a new life would be buried beneath a flood of bills, recriminations and I-told-you-so's. And most of all, while doing all that alone, she had to keep ever vigilant, ever ready for another confrontation with Bill Winslow, because one day soon he would be out, released. Every time she turned on the television she was reminded of this unpleasant fact.

She sighed, feeling resentful of anything and everything, but most of all resentful of the fact that *not* being vigilant meant her very life.

Unfortunately, all the vigilance and worry in the world didn't do much in the way of keeping her company. And when had she started missing it? Only recently. Before, she'd needed the confines of the Witness Protection Program, the forced seclusion. She'd needed the barriers that restricted her from active involvement in a community. She'd needed the time to heal, to regroup, to find herself again.

The women in her support network were nice enough, even eager to share time with her. But somehow that wasn't enough. Recently, occasionally, she found that she wanted to play a board game with a male instead of a female, craved hearing a deep rumble of laughter, wanted to tuck her hand in someone else's, to warm her chilly toes against the warm calf of a warmer man. These thoughts were almost shocking to her, for nothing in her life had ever been like that. She'd married Bill almost fresh out of college, a complete ingenue. An utter fool. And she'd spent the next ten years with him, having him prove that marriage was a nightmare instead of a promise.

But tonight, the fantasy tugged at her, insinuated itself into her thoughts, into her body. Tonight, she achingly wanted some male companionship. The stars were sharp and brilliant as they appeared suddenly in the upper sky, tempting and dazzling, making her want to stare up at them and wish, wish deeply and surely, wish with everything she had inside her. But what was the use in wishing? Dreams didn't come true unless you made them do so. And companionship came with too many strings. As a friend in her support group said, and as she knew all too well, there were much worse things than loneliness.

That was true. Kelsey knew it was true. And yet, it didn't feel all too absolutely right at the moment. Right now it seemed damned ridiculous, because sometimes there simply *weren't* worse things than loneliness. Sometimes loneliness was all there was.

She hadn't been on a date in what seemed like a million years. Not since she'd met Bill thirteen years ago, and even then, they hadn't really dated, he'd engulfed her in his bizarre fashion, taken her by overwhelming compulsion. She had almost accepted a couple of arranged evenings through members of her support group, but somehow, when the time came to follow through on the dates, she'd been unable to face a stranger across a table, whirl around some dance floor in the arms of someone who could turn out to be another Bill.

And she had an added factor she couldn't talk about, didn't even tell her support group about. For all that she was working to put her life in order, to take control of every aspect of daily living, she was constantly aware she was living a lie.

Her last name was legally hers, but she had neither been born with it nor married into it. Her records all showed her having been born in Pennsylvania; she hadn't been, she was born in Bethesda, Maryland. Her social security number was different, her college records were completely changed, though no one had thought to raise her grade-point average. And she had one notarized document most people never saw: her death certificate.

She could talk about Mr. Wrong, but wasn't she the female equivalent? Mr. Wrong lied about everything... nothing about her was the truth, not her name, her past, her records. Just her anger was real and bone deep.

Maybe it was that anger, the desire for the lies to be over, that sparked the loneliness in her tonight, making her restless in a way she hadn't felt for years, maybe hadn't ever really analyzed before.

Or maybe it was seeing the recent news accounts. A similar story to hers—a man trying to hire someone to kill his wife—had come out in the press only a few months ago. And now, according to the hungry reporters, apparently Bill was soon to be released. Naturally, they had paraded the whole sordid story across the screen, speculating on his motive, on his rehabilitation, and most of all, on her whereabouts.

Luckily she remained in hiding, no one had found her yet. But instead of pleasing her, this made her vaguely apprehensive. It gave her the feeling of living in the dark, a victim in the shadows.

Two nights ago had been the worst. National media announcers, on one of those in-depth reporting programs, had recapitulated what they had dubbed the Winslow Affair and, apparently totally unaware they were jeopardizing her whole life, had flashed three-year-old pictures of her on nationwide television. She hadn't been as firm and trim then, and she'd still been a blonde. But it didn't take a rocket scientist to see the resemblance. Several of her support group had called to comment on the uncanny coincidence of her having the same first name, remarkably similar features.

She'd become almost afraid to leave the house, reluctant to answer the telephone.

As if sensing her discomfort, the phone rang. Kelsey started, even felt for her ever-present .38 automatic at her side. She released an exasperated puff of disgust as she dropped her hand and went to the wall phone in the kitchen. She lifted it while pushing the sliding door closed again. She hesitated before saying hello. Her voice made the single word a question instead of a greeting.

"Kelsey?"

"Yes, Jilly." Just what she didn't want or need right now. There seemed to be one like Jilly in every group, a clinging vine that joined support groups less for survival techniques than for the thrill of being included, a person who thrived on the dirt and details of another's life. A person whose life was so incomplete she had to become over-involved in everyone else's just to believe she existed.

Unknowingly—or perhaps to stir the pot of some unknown contention—but striking pure fear into Kelsey nonetheless, Jilly immediately launched into an account of a talk show program she'd watched yesterday.

"It was all about women doing courageous things, like helping save children from their evil fathers. You should have seen it. They were talking all about the Winslow Affair. It gave me chills, and I really mean it."

"Really?" Kelsey asked, though it felt more forced than natural.

"Oh, Kelsey, it just broke my heart when I saw the picture they showed. It was a different one than the one they usually show on the news. I mean, I recognized you right off."

Dear God, Kelsey thought. "What do you mean, Jilly?" she asked. Her voice was as cold as her insides.

"Why, Kelsey, you don't have to keep it a secret from me. I'm one of your biggest fans. I mean, to have suffered what you did and to still want to help others. I mean, you're just terrific.''

Terrified was a lot closer to the truth. ''I'm afraid you've got the wrong idea—''

Jilly tittered. There was simply no other word for that grating sound. ''Now, now, Kelsey. I may be a lot of things, but my momma never raised any idiots. It's you, all right. That's what I told them, too.''

Kelsey felt as though she'd stepped into an elevator on the tenth level only to discover there was no floor. ''You what?''

''Oh, I didn't give you away, don't you go worrying about that. I mean, if you're hiding out, it's your business, isn't it?''

''What did you say?''

''There, you see? I just knew it. I knew I was right. I told them you were great, I mean, I said I knew this woman named Kelsey, and wasn't it a coincidence? You know, confusing them. But, anyway, I said you weren't a victim anymore. You were teaching other women how to stand up for themselves. And I could tell they were impressed.''

Oh, God. What had Jilly done?

''And I told them you had learned it all yourself. Taught yourself, I mean. I told them how you taught me so much, how I learned not to be a victim, either.''

Kelsey drew a shallow breath; it was all her compressed lungs would allow. ''That's amazing, Jilly. Did you happen to tell them where you live?''

''No, no, Kelsey. I told you, I was clever. I mean, I'd never do anything to hurt you. I just said I knew this woman in Texas—''

Kelsey couldn't hold in a groan.

''Oh, dear. Wasn't that okay? I mean, Texas is the largest state in the union. Except for Alaska . . . or is Texas bigger? I don't really know, do you?''

''Alaska's bigger,'' Kelsey said dully.

"Well, I wish you'd seen it, honey. You'd have been so proud of me. I mean, having the courage to actually call up Laurie Winters and talk to her on the phone in front of all those people."

"Yeah," Kelsey managed to get out.

"Did I interrupt something? Were you eating or anything?"

"Eating...yes. I was just sitting down," Kelsey said. Her heart was pounding so loudly she was half-afraid Jilly would hear it over the telephone.

"Well, gotta run myself. I'll tell you what, I'll call you later."

"No," Kelsey blurted out before she could think.

"No?"

"Tomorrow would be better, Jilly. I'm feeling a little under the weather. I'm just going to bed."

"Well, of course. I mean, with all you must be going through..."

"I'm not...going...through...*anything,* Jilly," Kelsey ground out through iron-clenched teeth. "You've made some amazing suppositions, but I have to tell you that—"

"Whoops, there's the doorbell. Gotta run, honey. Call you tomorrow, okay? Bye-bye, now. Take care."

Kelsey still had the phone to her ear, her mouth pursed to protest Jilly's all-too-accurate discovery, when she heard the sharp click of the receiver, the loud, nasal hum of the dial tone.

She replaced the receiver automatically, but didn't take her hand from it. As they said in Texas, her goose was good and cooked.

Wednesday, November 10
7:30 p.m., Berkeley Springs, West Virginia

Bill walked into the hotel lobby and looked around. The hotel clerk glanced up incuriously and back down to whatever he'd been doing. Too many tourists passed through Berkeley Springs to evince much interest, even at this evening hour in an off-season.

He crossed the lobby and took a seat against the far wall just beneath some plaque or other commemorating the brick as the same brick that George Washington had touched after taking a bath in the spa outside. George could have it, he thought, though the notion of a bath wasn't a bad one. Maybe he'd spring for one of the spa treatments himself. Later.

Now he just wanted to sit in this comfortable chair, let his hands play with the thick wad of cash in his pocket, and watch the front doors. He didn't have to watch long. It wasn't ten minutes before a young couple came in the front door, arm in arm, giggly and acting as though they'd just gotten married five minutes earlier. He smiled, even nodded at them as they passed him on their noisy way to the front desk.

The FBI was brighter than the guys in Hollywood made them look, he thought. But not bright enough. He'd seen the guy out in the car not ten minutes ago, hand wrapped around a cellular telephone. The girl had been sitting on a park bench, little makeup mirror in one hand, lipstick in the other. And eyes on anything but her image.

He rose slowly to his feet, gave a little stretch and deliberately crossed right in front of them to approach the desk clerk. He asked for a room. Signed for it in his own name, enjoying the game. Loving the game.

He asked the desk clerk about the hours at the spa. Since this was off-season, the clerk told him—and the eavesdropping newlyweds—he could get in anytime, but he'd better hurry, they folded up shop at nine.

"I think I'll try it now," he said, and sauntered off in the direction the clerk had pointed. It was out the back door of the hotel and around an elaborate series of corners and steps.

He chose the roman tub for two reasons, it was larger and he hadn't had anything like that kind of space in a tub for three long years, and because it was quiet. No jets, no bubbles, just silent, silent water. He could hear every single thing that happened in that whole spa. And he didn't have to listen long before the young man was ushered in and pretty soon being escorted to a tub just beyond his.

He smiled, and silently slipped from the water. Like a shadow, he curved around the corner of the hallway and into the change room. He had what he needed in less than a minute, transferred it to his own things, and was back into the water before his timer went off, signaling the spa attendant.

He endured a massage, though he hated being touched so intimately. He even talked to the young man when he came out of the tub and onto a table nearby. Yes, they'd married only that morning, the young man said. He even held out his hand to show the wedding ring on his left hand. And he waggled his fingers saying he still wasn't used to it being there. The hell he wasn't. He had a tan line revealing the ring had been there a good long time.

Having seen enough, Bill pushed from the table and didn't tip the masseuse. Though after his ride with the salesman he had plenty of operating capital, he'd never see this particular sadist again. He whistled as he dressed and continued the country-and-western tune as he left the spa facilities with the young man's clothing.

He felt good. He felt clean, fresh, and his mind seemed to be racing in swift, light harmony.

It only took a few seconds to find the honeymooner's room. He'd simply told the desk clerk that the young man had asked him to take his things to the young lady and to have her gather other clothing for him to take back to him. As pure luck would have it, she answered the door incautiously.

Using the FBI agent's gun—a nice touch, if he did say so himself—he asked the would-be bride to strip, enjoying a few seconds of frightening her, and tied her to the bathroom door. He took her clothes, as well. It wouldn't stop them. It wouldn't even slow them down for long. But he didn't need very long. Just a few minutes would do.

Yes, he was enjoying the game enormously.

He tossed their clothes out a window at the end of the long upstairs hallway. It would take a while to find them in all that shrubbery below. Especially in the dark. He chuckled.

Then, using a thin wire he'd taken from the salesman's trunk, he pried the lock of a room some doors down. He stretched out on the double bed and lay back, his hands folded behind his head.

He had only to wait.

And then he could begin his quest.

He smiled, thinking about Kelsey. *It won't be long now, sweetheart,* he promised. *And then you'll get everything you deserve.*

Wednesday, November 10
7:30 p.m., Lubbock, Texas

As the plane was circling over the golden tiara that made up Lubbock at night, the stewardess leaned over John's seat and handed him a folded message. "This came through a minute ago," she said. "You're to call this number as soon as you land. Unfortunately, we don't have in-plane communications," she added with a smile of apology.

John thanked her absently, flipping the paper open and reading the phone number as though it would reveal a clue as to the reason for the call. His orders were to go straight to Kelsey Winslow—Dobson—and remove her to a safe house. Simple, straightforward. Easy.

A message at this stage of the plan could only mean one thing: something was wrong.

John cursed the interminable time it seemed to take for the plane to finally touch down. He felt helpless up there in the dark sky, unable to do anything but wait.

What could be wrong?

Wednesday, November 10
8:30 p.m., Lubbock, Texas

Kelsey had already done her evening exercises, using them to work off the tension instead of pacing. In the few hours since Jilly had called, she had come to the inevitable conclusion that there wasn't a single thing she could do about Jilly's mistake now. With a survivor's fatalistic realism she had decided that what was done was in the past, that the only things worth worrying about were the present and the future.

But what if Bill had seen that program? And, like her so-called friend, put two and two together?

She had toyed with the idea of calling her case worker in Dallas, but had shaken that notion. If there was anything wrong, they'd be calling her. If she had anything to worry about, really worry about, they'd contact her.

Besides, she thought, Bill wasn't even a television watcher. He preferred to get his kicks out of his "deals," his scams, his destruction of other human beings. No, she was safe. As protected as anyone living a perpetual lie can ever be so considered.

For just a moment, a wild, totally crazy moment, she wished he actually would appear on her doorstep. That the continual running would finally be over and done with, finished. A classic showdown...him or her...once and for all, period, finis.

For this time around, Bill would have a few surprises in store for him. Kelsey wasn't the same scaredy-cat she'd been three years ago. He'd taught her the very valuable lesson of strength. Bill, who deemed her life valueless, and the judges who rated her life span at a mere three years, had conspired to create a strong Kelsey. Together they had forced her to change her life, her dreams, her plans.

Her life, as she had known it then, was truly over. Bill, for all that he might not know it, had succeeded in killing her. She'd left the house in Maryland, the house where she'd been raised; she'd left her job as an aerobics instructor; she'd left herself behind. All because she had known that a three-year sentence wouldn't even slow Bill down. He wasn't the kind of man who would take an indictment and sentencing as a judgment on his behavior. He would only see that he'd have to bide his time to accomplish his initial goal.

She suffered no illusions. Bill Winslow was crazy. The court-appointed psychologists may have encountered a few sociopathic tendencies, but Kelsey knew they hadn't even scratched the surface of Bill's personality. He had charmed them with his seeming remorse. She knew what they didn't: Bill Winslow didn't understand the meaning of the word.

And she knew that if he had the slightest clue where she was, nothing on earth would stop him from coming after her, and most likely, anyone who'd had anything to do with the sting operation that had pulled him into the open and behind bars. If he had the vaguest clue where she was hiding, it would only be a matter of days before he showed up, this time to do the job himself. That was the way he was. Once foiled, twice determined.

Luckily, three years ago, the FBI had listened to her. John Chandler, in particular, had believed what she'd said about Bill Winslow. He had arranged to have her slipped into the Witness Protection Program and quietly shipped out of the East. She certainly hadn't wanted to thank him at the time. She felt he was simply, conveniently, tucking her as far away from him as was humanly possible.

She tried shifting her thoughts to something else, anything other than that time three years ago. But it was hopeless. Once on that track, her mind couldn't seem to shift grooves. Her life might be different, everything about her might be altered, but some things simply didn't change. Her thoughts about the justice system, for one; Bill Winslow, for another. And John Chandler; she was still as confused about him as ever.

Like Bill, if John Chandler could see her now, he would be in for a big surprise. She was nearly as much a professional as he. She had long ago decided she needed to know what to do in *any* situation to protect herself.

And she'd spent the past three years learning how to do just that. The Kelsey of yesteryear was a rounder, tear-stained, blond version of the present-day Kelsey. Then, she'd have been hard-pressed to change a tire in less than an hour. Now, there was little she couldn't tackle. Then, she'd shrunk behind the very broad shoulders of FBI agent John Chandler when they'd heard a noise outside. Now, she held a black belt in karate, a brown in jujitsu and had even studied Korean kick-boxing. She had a personal arsenal of four perfectly timed weapons, and held an expert marksman's certificate to use each of them. Her home was as secure as any home could be with double dead-bolt locks, cinder block walls and automatic lighting. Even her business had to do with protection, teaching others how to do the same.

But she was the only person who would ever see those differences, the insecure Kelsey Winslow turned capable Kelsey Dobson. So John Chandler wouldn't be able to see the changes, wouldn't have another opportunity to hightail it out of her life. That notion should have pleased her, but didn't; it gave her a strangely hollow feeling deep inside.

Unconsciously, she raised her hand to her lips and pressed them, molding them to the grooves between her fingers while her mind recalled the one time John had kissed her. He had kissed her as though there was no day going to dawn the next morning, as though it was the farewell of an entire lifetime.

The doorbell rang and Kelsey dropped her hand guiltily, as if she'd been caught with her phantom, with a memory now three years old and surely sepia toned with time and imperfect recall.

With Jilly's revelation on her mind, the recent news accounts clamoring in her heart, she lightly raced across the Saltillo-tiled hallway, pausing only to release the safety of her .38 automatic, but leaving it in her belt holster. She pushed the doors of her highboy closed, hiding the computer center, not from any particular fear it might be harmed, but more from sheer habit of maintaining strict routine.

She crossed the broad foyer and cautiously stepped out the front door into the eastern interior courtyard and slowly covered the some thirty feet to the exterior gate. She flipped the catch on the little wooden window inset in the huge wooden gate recessed in the ten-feet high adobe walls. She slowly pulled it inward and drew her gun. She held it at the ready as she stepped into the frame the small window created.

Light spilled outward, highlighting the man on the other side.

Kelsey actually felt the blood draining from her face.

Chapter 3

John Chandler tensed as the little window in the huge barricade of a gate slowly swung open. He felt an agent's atavistic fear of that narrow aperture. It conjured too many memories of movie scenes where the bad guys shot through just such an opening, firing first, asking questions later.

The window was like everything else about this new residence of Kelsey's—different. Her Texas home seemed to sprawl across the huge corner lot, a seeming Spanish villa, complete with whitewashed walls, thick, red ceramic tiles stretching upward to form a sloping roofline, arched entries barricaded by thick wooden gates, tall, age-thickened cacti and other spiny succulents sending spiking tendrils toward windows, clay gutters and unsuspecting intruders. The entire place was surrounded by tall, thick, uneven adobe walls, hand-swirled with a creamy white stucco. The effect was one of Southwestern luxury, of serenity and abject privacy. It was also as forbidding a place as John had ever seen.

Heavy wrought-iron bars covered every window visible on the second floor. The huge wooden gate with its miniature opening stood in the rough center of the walls surrounding the place, but John didn't think it led inside the house, merely into another yard. Like everything else, it was more appearance than reality; it, like the house itself, was a door within a door, a cell within a cell. It was a rabbit warren of a home, self-protective.

And it was a far cry from Kelsey's redbrick Colonial in Bethesda with its little window boxes filled with winter flowers, holly, poinsettia, and on the inside, herbs and pansies. The effect of that house had been orderly, sweet, even a little prim. Like Kelsey.

Would the woman be as altered as her surroundings?

While he'd been waiting for someone—Kelsey?—to answer his ring, he had tried thinking what he would say to her. Seeing him would be shock enough; hearing he was once again assigned to her might really frighten her. And hearing his news would scare the living daylights out of anyone, let alone Kelsey.

He could all too easily remember her wide blue eyes, the faint shadows beneath them, the look of a woman pushed too far, pressed against the proverbial wall. Yes, he would have to tread carefully.

He'd have to be careful for other reasons, too, he thought grimly. Reasons entirely personal. Her very helplessness, her dependency had once acted on him like the strongest of aphrodisiacs. And simple want all too often became equated with need.

Now the window was fully open, showing him a glimpse of the spacious, Spanish-style home beyond an interior garden of some kind. But no one stood there. For a split second, John felt as if he'd rung the doorbell of a ghost. Was he too late?

He couldn't help the tension that gripped his shoulders and seized his back as a shadow crossed the lighted aperture and the silhouette of a woman's face appeared.

She stepped back a pace at seeing him there, and the light fell on her features, touching her suddenly wide eyes, her parted lips, and creating a blue-black halo of her hair.

Kelsey. Just as he remembered her. Oh, yes, he'd have to tread very carefully, indeed.

She stood there for the longest time, neither moving nor speaking. John couldn't have spoken, either; his breath felt trapped in his lungs, his heartbeat thundered in his ears. *Kelsey.* Until he was actually seeing her again, he realized he hadn't given total consideration to how he might feel at being in her presence. He knew now. Confused. Nobody should have the kind of chemistry that made another's body go nuts. But Kelsey did.

John had envisioned ringing the doorbell tucked in the hand-swirled mass of creamy stucco, had even imagined feeling the rough plaster scratch at his fingertips. He had tried picturing Kelsey as she might be today, tonight. But now, facing her through the narrow window in a heavy gate, inches away but separated by a three-year absence, John could only stand there, hands loose at his sides as though ready for a fight.

He saw her eyes widen even more in recognition and flinched slightly as he read the measure of her surprise, her profound shock at seeing him again.

"Oh, God," she said.

He nodded and forced an apologetic smile to his frozen lips. He'd seen her understanding of why he was there flash across her features like a brushfire. She'd realized instantaneously that this was no three-year-delayed social call.

"Hello, Kelsey," he said.

"John Chandler," she murmured. His name on her lips wasn't a question, it was a breathless statement of truth. He couldn't glean any more from her voice than simple acknowledgment of who he was.

"Can I come in?" he asked. Even to himself, his voice sounded hoarse, rough with a thousand conflicting, contradictory emotions. And harsh with pity.

They had named each other now, he thought. He felt a vague relaxation work through his shoulders; naming was the most basic of human interaction. I know you, you know me, now we can communicate. It was the first thing given to a child, the last thing etched on the gravestone. The initial hurdle was over.

For a moment she did nothing more than stare at him as if he were the ghost. Perhaps he was, he thought; a ghost of a memory from her past. Then, startling him, she slowly closed the little window in the gate, cutting the light, shutting him out.

For some reason the sheer finality of that closure made John smile. She hadn't slapped his face or pretended she hadn't recognized him. She'd named him, then calmly shut the little window, leaving the bigger gate closed, shutting him out, effectively putting him outside her life.

"We've got to talk, Kelsey," he called, knowing instinctively that she was still there, just on the other side of that monstrosity of a gate.

She didn't answer and John was reaching for the doorbell again when he heard the catch on the gate; a raspy, metal-on-metal sound of a heavy dead-bolt release. The large door swung slowly inward while the light crept into the dark, forming a pool of gold at his feet.

Kelsey stood beyond the door's swing, facing him, legs slightly spread, her hands on her hips, her body blocking the light, creating a silhouette of her lithe frame. Whatever she was wearing was so skintight it made her appear nude in that light. Nude, that was, except for the holster on her hip and the weapon tucked neatly inside it.

She was the very image of a warrior, something out of a Frazetta fantasy painting, all curves, muscles and weapon. John realized now that her dark halo of hair hadn't been a trick of the light, she had jet black hair, loosely drawn up to a ponytail, so long it snaked around one shoulder. All Kelsey needed to complete the image of one of Frazetta's vibrant fantasy paintings would be a saber-toothed tiger at her side, or a dragon lurking in her backyard.

Oh, yeah, he thought. Kelsey had changed.

But then he could see the quick rise and fall of her chest, the tense shoulders.

"I didn't think I'd ever see you again," she said, her sultry contralto voice no longer at variance with her appearance. Always before, that rich voice had seemed somewhat out of place with her sweet, frightened features, Dresden hair and eyes. But this dark shadow packing a gun, legs askance, shoulders back and rigid, had to have a voice that made a man want to fall to his knees.

Somehow he managed to step across the gate threshold. But he did so with the very real feeling that he was the willing fly following a siren black widow.

Kelsey was reeling. For one wild moment, seeing John Chandler standing there on her doorstep, she'd had the sharpest feeling that he'd come there just to see her. Three years and he appears on a night when she'd stood outside wishing on the millions of stars in the Texas sky.

But a measure of pity, a certain hard set to his jaw, a faint glint of steel in his gaze stole this piercing wish even as it flashed across her mind. She knew instinctively that it was no coincidence that John Chandler had shown up on her doorstep. He'd obviously come on official business. And knowing this, she knew what that business was. Bill must have been released.

And her life was in danger again.

Unbidden came the phrase, *It's show time*. And with that thought came the fear. Three years of training, of building her strength, of safeguarding her life, and a face out of her past immediately throws her into chaos.

But surely Bill's release wouldn't occasion an FBI agent ringing her doorbell? Unless . . . Bill had some notion of her whereabouts. And she knew the answer to that one, also. By some stroke of the most evil luck, he'd seen or heard about that damned television program Jilly had called about.

And Bill's having seen it would only mean one thing: he'd be after her.

Kelsey squared her shoulders. She again resolved not to dwell on any regretful aspects of that interview. What was done, was done. Now she had to face John Chandler and wasn't sure how she felt about the prospect. There was too much between them and far too little. And all of it was wrapped up in the package bearing Bill Winslow's name and deeds. She couldn't think of John Chandler without remembering the entire ordeal three years ago. And she couldn't separate him from the anger that still boiled inside her. And still couldn't quite forgive him for one kiss at a vulnerable moment, nor the unforgivable regret she'd glimpsed in his eyes afterward.

She led him into her house, walking slowly and steadily, but feeling dazed and nervous. She couldn't think of what to say to him, and he didn't help her at all, merely followed her silently. He still moved as quietly as a cat, as lithely as a gymnast.

He stopped when she did, and she found she couldn't meet his eyes. He looked away, surveying her living quarters.

She had thought she remembered everything about John Chandler, from his warm eyes to his hard, flat stomach and narrow, tapered hips. She watched him as he stood perfectly still, eyes taking in everything, studying her living room, her kitchen, her Southwestern-style dining table, as though he were inventorying it for the Bureau. And she discovered she'd forgotten all the essential elements that made up John Chandler.

His eyes were still brown, the color of Kentucky bourbon, and fine laugh lines still fanned out from them. His hair was the same raw-honey brown, and if there was any gray there, it didn't show. He'd be forty now, but was the same fighting trim, the same early thirties hard. His lips were still full and firm looking, though she knew them to be as soft and pliant as a fresh rose just beginning to bloom. He was as tall and muscled as ever. But it was none of those things that had eluded her memory. It was the way he made her stomach knot in hot anxiety. It was the way he made her hands shake, her loins ache.

Her memory had carefully stored every feature, every detail of John Chandler, but had, perhaps equally carefully, erased the impact he had on *her*. She had to deliberately turn her back on him, find something to do at the kitchen bar counter. She didn't want to feel such things for anyone, and John Chandler in particular. He'd made it all too clear three years ago where she stood with him and that was somewhere out in the cold. That was fine with her. That's exactly where she wanted him to be, too. Now.

If only he didn't make her feel anything but cold.

"Why are you here?" she asked finally, even though she had no doubts as to his reason. But the silence between them was fraught with too few memories, too many possibilities.

"Your ex-husband's out," he said.

She'd known what he was going to say, had even tensed in anticipation, but his speaking the words aloud, the words she'd dreaded thinking about for the past three years, still managed to make her flinch.

She turned around to face John, needing to see him, needing to see the truth in his eyes. She knew he wasn't lying, yet everything in her wanted to scream a denial.

"It's too early," she said.

A bitter smile crooked one side of his lips. His eyes met hers directly, unwaveringly. "Good behavior," he said.

An answering bitterness made her own lips curl, but she didn't think it would resemble a smile. "Only Bill."

"I've been assigned to your case," he said. "We've got a safe house lined up."

She met his gaze squarely, searching for anything that would give her a clue as to what his assignment might entail. She could read his confusion, his disturbed reaction to the changes in her, and saw him trying to fuse the old Kelsey with the new. He might as well give it up, she thought, not without bitterness. That Kelsey was long gone.

She slowly turned back around, unable to continue to watch his search. Unable to look into his eyes and see herself as he wanted to see her, the frail, poor little Kelsey, all alone, so helpless. But all questions were answered now. John Chandler was once again assigned to be her nursemaid, to be her faceless knight in shining armor, prepared to tilt his sword, tip his helmet and slay her dragon. And then he would ride away into some rosy sunset, never giving her another thought.

She'd be damned if he would. She was perfectly capable of slaying her own dragons, thank you very much. She didn't stop to think if she was angry over his coming to protect her, or his inevitable abandonment. She wouldn't have cared to analyze it. She'd been down the path of that particular fantasy once already; she wasn't about to go through it again.

"I'm perfectly fine," she said through clenched teeth. She tried seeing it from his perspective. Tried thinking of him as a kind, gentle soul who cared only for her safety, but she couldn't. She could only think of his being assigned to protect her; she could only see herself as an *object* needing a week or two of special care.

She remembered the cold light in his eyes the morning after he'd kissed her. She remembered, all too well, his stark admission that he was married, the fingers all but digging into her arms. And she remembered his distance, his wary stance whenever she walked into a room after that. *And* she remembered, as though it were yesterday, his answer to her question of why he hadn't told her before that he was married. "It should never have happened."

He was right, it shouldn't have. And it never would again. She had been crying when he'd kissed her, she remembered that also, and recalled more tears after that. But her tears had dried long ago, about the time the old Kelsey had died. She had her anger to see her through now.

"I'm not going anywhere," she said slowly, not looking at him. Although her voice was adamant, she couldn't help a rather forlorn wish that John would somehow manage to defuse the anger that sustained her, that he would somehow whisk her away, catch Bill, and with a wave of some magic wand, set her life to rights again once and forever.

But like the old Kelsey, Cinderella daydreams of someone "taking her away from all this" were long dead. Her life now was one forged in the fires of pure survival, the hard world of bills, mortgage payments and anger.

"Kelsey—" John began, a combined note of patronizing patience and exasperation.

"I'm not running," she interrupted. When she'd decided that, she couldn't have said. It might have been when she realized he was still looking at her as if she were some poor little thing who couldn't fend for herself, or it might have happened that first earned belt in karate, or earlier, the day she'd really looked at her haggard, dull face in the bathroom mirror of a bleak apartment and known she couldn't go on that way.

"You don't have much choice," he said.

She turned at that and smiled somewhat bitterly. "You're wrong, John. I have all the choice in the whole world."

He frowned heavily. "Look, Winslow might have pulled a good-behavior release, but he's no picnic. He told one of his cellmates he was coming after you."

Kelsey felt a chill work down her back. If the FBI, namely John Chandler, hadn't stepped in three years ago, Bill Winslow would have succeeded in his attempt on her life. And now that same rescuer was back, and again telling her she couldn't manage things by herself, that she needed him, that her life wasn't worth the proverbial plug nickel.

She withheld a shudder of revulsion and hardened her heart against the notion of John Chandler being able to rescue her. It wouldn't do to start relying on somebody else at this time, or anytime. She had first-hand experience in the futility of trust, the frustration and pain of watching that trust erode.

"There's no argument about this, Kelsey. I have my orders. So do you."

"Only if I choose to remain in the program," she said. She felt more resolve now. She knew she had to do this. She couldn't bear the thought of running away again. She'd come too far, with too much of her heart vested in the attempt. Running now would make her a victim once again.

"No," she said, and meant everything the negative could imply.

"You're in, and so far as we can, we're going to make sure you're safe."

Duty. That was all she meant to him. All she'd ever meant. She'd known that, had accepted it years ago, but hearing it implied all-over-again hurt just the same.

"Well, you've told me," she said coldly.

"And I can turn around and go straight to hell, is that it?" he asked, and grinned. But it wasn't a lighthearted gesture and he didn't so much as move a muscle toward the door.

She had to smile at his more than accurate assessment of her words, but it was a faint attempt at best. "Something like that," she answered levelly.

"Have you gone suicidal on me?" His tone was one of friendly, even casual interest, and belied the import of the words.

How could she have forgotten that John Chandler didn't have much use for tact? Instead of angering her, his stark question steadied her. "I haven't gone anything on *you.*"

He looked at her for a long, utterly still moment, and she could see him assimilating the implications of her emphasis on the pronoun. He said quietly, "Winslow's already shaken two sets of tails today. So, if you'll please go pack a bag, I've got the address of the safe house. And then we'll wait."

"How long?"

"How long . . . what?"

"How long would we wait?"

"A week, two? Maybe more."

"Until the FBI is sure he won't show, or until he knocks on my door here? I presume you'll have a team watching my place?"

"Yeah," he affirmed, his eyes puzzled.

"And what if he doesn't come?"

A light flashed in his eyes as she saw him think he understood what she was after. "We wouldn't leave you on your own unless we were damned sure he wouldn't be a threat."

She swallowed a sharp retort. He'd made that same promise three years ago. And here he was again. Because Bill was after her again. So much for promises.

"You won't have to worry about anything," he said.

"Because you'll catch the bad guy," she said, and couldn't hold back the dull edge from her voice.

"If possible, yes."

Yes, she thought. If possible, if *necessary.* He had caught the bad guy three years ago. He'd held her in his strong arms and comforted her, reassured her that everything would be all right. And lonely, desperate, scared beyond thought, she'd responded to the sheer maleness of him, the strengths, the vulnerabilities she'd glimpsed in him, and had allowed him to see her own weaknesses, those weaknesses that were all on the surface back then.

But the justice system had decided that the bad guy need only be sidetracked for a few years, a breather in the life of a man determined to kill her. And the good guy, *this* good guy, had stayed only long enough to hear the sentence before running three-thousand miles away from her. Another assignment, back on the road, he'd said. Back to his life, back to the arms of the wife he hadn't told her about. His wife.

What did he want from her now? Were too many sleepless nights spent regretting a single kiss supposed to make her receptive to his return?

The trouble was, she thought half-coherently, her body was all too receptive. Her heart was still beating in an irregular rhythm, an unsyncopated thrum. And her lips felt dry and in need of moisture. As she ran her tongue between them, she realized they were dry not in nervousness but in some bizarre anticipation. As fresh as though it were yesterday, she could feel his lips upon hers, his hot breath upon her cheek.

He seemed to invade her house, infusing it with his scent—that same heady, musky scent—and making it smaller by his sheer presence, his certainty that she would do whatever he ordered, a willing soldier to his commanding tone.

Packing a bag and slinking out of her own home, a home she had fought for, won with long, hard work and determination, simply wasn't an alternative. The old Kelsey would have done as he dictated, no questions asked. But that Kelsey was dead and buried. And John Chandler had orchestrated her epitaph.

She wondered whether she would have felt so affected, so adamant about not leaving her home if it had been any other agent who had shown up on her doorstep. Was she simply reacting to the pity, the memory of the old, fragile Kelsey in his eyes that made her want to prove him wrong?

Thinking this, wondering about it, she tried offering some measure of courtesy, if only as a reward for informing her that Bill was out. If only because he'd tried helping her three years ago and had succeeded in irrevocably changing her life. Courtesy, maybe, but did she have to thank him? She didn't think so.

She gestured to one of the heavy oak dining chairs. He didn't move and she was forced to meet his eyes again. She wasn't sure what the message in his gaze portended, but she was suddenly, sharply aware of their being alone in her large house, alone in the night.

"What's going on here, Kelsey?" he asked.

"Won't you sit down?" she asked in return.

"No. I just want to get a handle on what I'm seeing."

She turned away from him and walked into the spacious, open kitchen. She hoped that he couldn't see how nervous he made her feel. She unlatched the buckled holster and laid the gun on the bar counter.

"That, for instance," he said.

"My bar?" she asked lightly, although she felt anything but lighthearted. "Or the .38?"

He didn't say anything and she didn't turn around from her retrieval of two glasses to see his reaction. She had the distinct feeling she was playing with fire when trying to banter with John Chandler, a man who hadn't minced words three years ago, had seemed to grow even harder in the interim.

"Orange juice or iced tea?" she asked. "Or would you like something stronger?"

"Stronger," he said. And she could have sworn he muttered, "I'm gonna need it."

She made him a Scotch and water over ice and poured herself a glass of lemon-flavored iced tea. She wanted to keep her wits about her. Last night, last week, she would have said it was necessary because he'd just told her Bill Winslow was out there somewhere and undoubtedly coming after her. But tonight she knew it was because of John Chandler, standing like a statue, eyeing her dining room like a panther might stare at a loose rod in his cage.

"Some dippy woman practically gave out your address on national television yesterday," he said as she handed him his drink.

There it was. Thanks, Jilly. Whatever she'd said on the talk show had been as bad as Kelsey had gleaned from their rambling conversation. Something in Jilly's spew of misinformation had tipped somebody off. She *had* been recognized.

"One of the women in one of the support groups," Kelsey said quietly.

"Well, tell her for me that with friends like her, you sure don't need any enemies."

"She's a lonely, confused woman," Kelsey said repressively. Or was it defensively?

"She's an idiot. And so are you for telling her who you are."

Kelsey didn't stop to guard her tongue nor did she hesitate to meet his eyes now. "I didn't tell her a damned thing! She's the kind of busybody who makes it her business to figure out everything and anything. Most of the time she's so far off base that no one would dream of listening to her!"

"I thought you said she was a lonely, confused woman," he said. A grin lifted one side of his mouth.

"I don't have to defend myself to you or anyone else," Kelsey said. Like her other statement, it sounded all too defensive. She wanted to tell him that it was her life, he hadn't been around when she'd had to grapple with the hardships involved in the program, and he had no right to question her. But saying all that might sound as if she were looking for pity, and that was the last thing she'd want from John Chandler. The very last thing.

"I followed standard procedure," she said. "I never took a step without the express permission of the program case workers. No one's recognized me in three years. Not until those news accounts," she added with some bitterness.

"It was only a matter of time after the newspeople got hold of your picture again."

She frowned a question.

"Hell, Kelsey, you can dye your hair, you can change your last name. But let's face it, you would have to wear a Halloween mask and gain two hundred pounds before someone who knew you wouldn't recognize you," he said dryly. "And even then I'd have my doubts."

Kelsey's breath caught in her throat again. Something about the way he said it made her feel naked. "Did you?" she asked.

"Have my doubts?"

"Recognize me."

He didn't answer for a minute, his eyes slowly taking her in. "Black hair doesn't change you all that much."

She could tell he was lying. And the realization pleased her for some reason.

"I think it does," she said.

When he didn't speak, she met his eyes again and was immediately sorry. Whatever the reason for his comment, and however much his arrival on her doorstep might have been caused by Bill Winslow's release, his thoughts weren't on Bill now. She didn't know how or why she knew that, she just did. And she doubted his thoughts were even on the safe house or the possible lengthy custodial duty.

He looked away before she could probe any further. He stared out her double-barred patio doors to the broad garden and lawn beyond, a dark field lit only by tiki lights. She saw his eyes take in the high, stucco-covered adobe wall that surrounded the grounds. And she saw the russet stain that colored his cheeks, the back of his neck.

"Three years seems like a very long time ago," she said finally. His eyes slowly shifted to meet hers.

"I wonder if Winslow feels the same way."

She felt as though he'd slapped her.

"Why don't we cut the small talk, Kelsey? Go pack a bag or two."

"No."

He sighed. "Look...I don't want to argue. I just want to get you to safety. Okay?"

"No."

"I knew this was a mistake," he said, though Kelsey was fairly sure he wasn't speaking to her.

She wanted to ask him to be more specific, but was more than half-afraid what his answer might be. She felt a strange, nearly foreign tug at the heartstrings she thought stilled forever. His expression was distant, but more sorrow filled than angry.

She sat down at the table, placing her heated palms against the cool oak. Now he sat down, as well, moving as though his back hurt him and Kelsey remembered him telling her that he'd been assigned to her case all those years ago because he was recuperating from a bullet wound. Another case. Another lifetime ago that she'd heard about it. Still, perversely, she found herself wishing there was something she could do to ease that pain. What was it about him that seemed to stir the old Kelsey emotions? Was he just a reminder of the past? Or was it because he was one of the few people on earth who knew her past, her life, her *name?*

"Tell me why you don't want to go to a safe house," he said. His tone suggested that he would listen to her reasons, then lay some sanity on her. It raised her hackles.

"You've seen this house. I'm safer here than I would be at any 'safe' house. If Bill's going to show up, I'd rather deal with him on my own turf."

"That's hooey. And you know it. You can't *deal* with someone like Winslow."

"I'm tired of running," she said heavily. Honestly.

"Tired of running or tired of living?" he asked harshly.

John saw Kelsey flinch at his words as though he'd struck her, and hated himself for having hurt her. That was the very last thing he wanted to do. But what was he supposed to do? Take her cold advice and let her be? He wasn't much in the persuasion department, he was more used to action than words, but this called for some of that nonexistent charm Charlie liked to kid him about. He had to make her understand that she was no more safe here than she'd been in Bethesda when her ex hired a hit man to kill her.

"Kelsey," he said, trying by tone to convey his sympathy for her, his need to have her listen to what she was saying. But even to himself his voice sounded hard, as cold as hers had been. He wanted to say a million different things, some of which had nothing to do with Bill Winslow or the events that had occurred three years ago—except one.

"It's no use trying to talk me into going," she said softly, her rich contralto voice lingering in the air like a scent.

As it had every time she'd spoken during those two months, three years earlier, her voice played on his spine like a sonata, making him stiffen his resolve against a desire to take her in his arms and damn the consequences. He'd made that mistake once, he wasn't likely to repeat it. And judging by the grim set of her features, she wasn't likely to let him try.

"But thanks for telling me Bill's out. It's a good safety tip."

John didn't find her words amusing. If anything, he found them poignant. It was a simple statement of fact telling him that she'd been hurt by one too many people, felt a complete lack of trust in other's abilities to help her. Her words also spelled out the distance between she and John and strengthened his notion that she wasn't interested in shortening that gap.

But he wasn't about to just accept her decision to stay. He hadn't been kidding when he called it suicide. Trying to face down a maniac such as Winslow was exactly that.

"Kelsey . . . we have to talk."

"There's nothing to talk about," she said somewhat defiantly. "I know Jilly may have thrown a wrench in the works by going on television like that—" She raised her hand as if he'd been about to interrupt her. The gesture was unnecessary, he couldn't have spoken if she'd held him at gunpoint. She was taking this far too casually, way too easily. He felt as though he were talking to a dark-haired twin of Kelsey's, a twin who didn't have the foggiest notion what she was up against.

"But what's done is done. And in a way, I'm glad she did it."

"What!"

She nodded, her long, silky ponytail flipped off her shoulder. John wondered if it still felt the same, would it feel as soft in black?

"Maybe I'm relieved that all this subterfuge is at an end," she said, and met his gaze squarely. "Do you have any idea how hard it is to get control of your life when your entire existence is a *lie?*"

John shook his head, though he had a fairly good idea.

"Do you know what I do for a living? I teach women how to take control of their lives. I teach them self-defense. I teach them how to spot a lie a country mile away. And the whole time I'm doing that I'm *lying* to them. Sometimes I even start believing those lies myself."

"Are you blaming me for that, Kelsey?" John asked quietly when she'd wound down.

She looked at him steadily. "Partially, yes."

"Because I got you in the Witness Protection Program?"

"Because you didn't kill Bill Winslow when you had the chance."

If she had kicked him in the stomach, he couldn't have been more surprised. He had imagined many conversations with Kelsey, some wholly in the fantasy realm, but he'd never have envisioned this one.

He glanced at the gun on her counter, back over at her fighting-trim body, up to her defiant glare. "You tell me when I had that chance," he said.

"When he showed up with the money."

"He was unarmed."

"He had hired someone to kill me," she said.

"And he went to prison for that."

"For three years. Big deal."

"Kelsey . . . he didn't succeed."

"No? Then what would you call having to creep out of town in the middle of the night, move to a city where you don't know a single soul, where you wake up in the morning with a different name, a different background, a different life? I call that overwhelming success."

John was trying to keep his own temper down. Of all the twisted thinking. For Christ's sake, he'd saved her *life*. She may have had to alter a few details, but she was around to do that, wasn't she? He ran a hand through his thick hair, trying to keep his mouth shut despite the fact she was damning every single good thing he thought he'd done for her.

"You can call it whatever you like," he said through his teeth. "But I still see Kelsey when I look across this table. And no matter how dark your hair is, no matter how angry you've become, and no matter how much you might think this is my fault—and let me tell you that really ticks me off—you still got a tongue to lash me with, a mouth to spew all this out of. I don't call that dead at all."

When she'd first opened that gate, his memory had fused his recollection of her over her features. Then he'd seen that Frazetta silhouette, a gun-packing shadow.

Now he was forced to look again. To see her clearly. She was still as beautiful, inky black hair pulled back in a modified ponytail that made her look more like a teenager than a woman of thirty-something, large blue eyes that conjured up images of Sunday mornings in bed, laughing at an old movie, warm fires in winter. Her figure was still superlative, though slimmer than he remembered or normally liked, and her long legs, encased in those tight, shiny stretch things, certainly were as elegantly curved as before. Yet she was different. All-over different.

For one thing, an expensive holster rested on her bar with a .38 caliber pistol nestled inside it and he'd seen her wearing it like a pro. John didn't know too many women who sat around chewing out FBI agents, a gun lying on their kitchen counter so casually that it might as well have been one of her copper pans.

For another, the Kelsey of three years ago had hardly said boo to any of the boys, let alone argued with them. This Kelsey was almost literally loaded for bear.

She sighed and looked away from him. Her eyes were luminous with unshed tears, but they weren't the tears of fear, the kind she'd shed three years ago. These were the evidence of her unresolved anger, her frustration, and perhaps, even a tinge of guilt for lashing out at him.

He realized, more on a subliminal level than with any real conscious thought, that the differences in Kelsey weren't merely physical or even mental. They were thorough, fundamental. Endemic. No fear had shown in her eyes, her steady gaze, her poise, when he'd told her Bill Winslow was out. She hadn't responded with a tremor in her voice, a trembling in her lip. She'd asked him *why* he'd come to Lubbock.

And she'd answered his bitter remark about Bill Winslow with an echoing bitterness. But then he'd caught her slight smile. Had he seen that particular smile on an agent's lips he would have said the agent was looking forward to an encounter of some kind. He couldn't help glancing over at the weapon on the bar again. She'd said she was tired of living a lie, tired of running. Did that also mean she was planning to settle things with Winslow once and for all?

The notion almost made him smile. If that was what she was after, little, fragile Kelsey Winslow had become one tough cookie. And if it were true, he found he couldn't blame her one bit. If he were in her shoes, he'd be heartily sick of running, of lying, of waiting for a knock on the door that could mean the end of security, could even mean the end of living.

But surely she could see that *thinking* about a confrontation with someone such as Winslow was a whole world different than actually *doing* it?

"Kelsey, look, I know how difficult this all must have been for—"

"No, you don't," she interrupted coldly. Her gaze shifted to his. All evidence of tears was gone. A wicked light danced in the fathomless blue, a hot fire. "You don't know anything about it. Nobody who hasn't died and tried to rebuild a life out of the ashes can possibly know."

"Look," he said. "I didn't come here to make you angry."

"Then why have you come, John? Do you have direct information that Bill knows where I am?"

"He saw that television program your girlfriend gabbed on."

"So?"

Her seemingly honest confusion puzzled John. She couldn't be so naive as to think that Bill Winslow would simply fade into obscurity, leave her alone? She had been the one to convince John and a host of other FBI agents that Winslow was a man without a conscience. Surely she couldn't have changed this much?

The gun on her counter told him she recognized the danger. That was no toy or prop she hauled around; that was the real McCoy. A deadly reality.

"Damn it, Kelsey. Winslow's a first-class nut case! You're the one that convinced *me!* I believed you when you said he'd come after you the first chance he got. The man's as dangerous as a rattlesnake. And we've *lost* him. Don't you get it? The man is deadly!"

At his words, her eyelids narrowed slightly, and again, puzzling him even more, that faint smile played on her lips.

"So am I, John."

He could only stare at her. Finally he leaned forward until there were only three or four inches separating them. She didn't flinch so much as an iota. "The man wants to *kill* you, Kelsey."

"Nothing has changed, then," she said flippantly.

His hand shot out without his even being aware of it. He grabbed her slender wrist and forced her to meet his gaze. She met it coolly. He wanted to shake her until she backed down, until she said she understood what he was trying to tell her.

Or was it until she begged him for mercy? he asked himself acidly. What did that make him? But damn it, she shouldn't look at him as if *he* were the cause of her troubles.

"Are you going to let me go?" she asked.

"No," he answered immediately. "Not until you listen to me."

"I am listening. I don't see that you need to touch me while I do so."

She said it so stiffly, so primly, that John wanted to laugh out loud. Pistols for two, but take your filthy hands off me, you evil man. He didn't release her. He even shook her wrist a little. "You may think you're hearing me, but you're obviously not taking in my meaning. We had an informant in the cell with Winslow the last couple of months before his release. Pete likened your ex to a wolverine, Kelsey. That's an animal that kills for the pure pleasure of it.''

She looked down at his hand grasping her wrist. She said nothing but the chill emanating from her was such that he slowly released her. To his self-disgust, he saw the red-marked evidence of his grip on her wrist. She didn't rub it or acknowledge it in any way. The look on her face stilled his instinctive apology.

''I got all that,'' she said icily. ''I just don't understand where the FBI fits in all this.''

And suddenly John understood. Like a blinding flash it came to him. What was going on with Kelsey wasn't just a notion, it was the farthest thing from any daydream.

Her stiffened shoulders, her cool expression, they hadn't been because of him; they'd had to do with Winslow. The locks on her gate, *the gun on her hip*...they all added up to one thing. Kelsey might be different, but with good reason. She'd been trained the hard way not to trust anybody. She hadn't forgotten what Winslow was like...far from it. She remembered better than anyone ever should have to, the fact that her husband had wanted her dead. She knew her friend had made a serious blunder by going on television, and now that she knew for certain Bill had seen the program, she *knew* he would be coming after her.

And she understood perfectly well there was only so much the law could do to protect her. She'd made her home into a fortress, her body lithe and quick, and she wore a holster with a gun tucked inside and took it off with the smooth motion of someone who has learned to eat, breathe and sleep with it. *Kelsey had gone into the business of taking care of herself.*

He felt a shaft of admiration for her shoot through him, warming him for the first time since he'd entered her house. It was hard to give up his memory of Kelsey as a sweetly trembling, frightened woman, a woman who needed big, tough John Chandler around for protection. But, in many ways, the changes, differences, carried an allure all their own.

"Kelsey," he said softly, looking her straight in the eyes, "I am here to help you. And I'm going to do just that. If you don't like it, you can request another agent."

He saw the flicker in her eyes but continued as though he hadn't noticed. "It doesn't make a damn bit of difference to me one way or the other," he lied. "But someone is going to get you out of here. And since I know you, and you know me, such as it is, and more important, since I know Bill Winslow, I'm suggesting you give in and accept the situation."

"I'll make a deal with you," she said steadily.

"What?" he asked warily.

"You stay . . . but we stay here."

"Damn it—"

"Otherwise, I'll just show you the door."

"I can place you under protective custody," he threatened.

"Arrest me, you mean?"

"Yes."

"That's the only way I'll go out that door, and trust me, John, everybody in Lubbock would hear me screaming."

John couldn't help smiling a little. He didn't have a doubt she would carry out her counterbluff. Nonetheless, he asked, "And what purpose would that serve?"

"It would let Bill know exactly where I am. And he'd come. And I'd kill him."

John didn't dare let her see how her dark statement rocked him. This had turned from a simple game of out-bluffing the bluffer to some deadly intent. He saw her eyes widen as she took in her own words, the meaning behind them. And then he saw her assume the mantle of purpose. How many times had he done the same thing, said he'd get the guy, then feel the determination come on the heels of the statement?

Charlie Fulghum was going to love hearing about this one, he thought. He realized he'd be glad to switch places with Charlie right about now. He'd rather be chasing after UFOs any day than sitting across from this lovely woman with murder on her mind. Especially when all he wanted to do was gather her into his arms and hold her until that tension drained from her shoulders.

If Charlie were here, John thought, trying to think of anything but the mental image he'd conjured up, Charlie would pull some razzle-dazzle on Kelsey and she'd be trotting along to the safe house, trusting Charlie to take care of everything. But Charlie wasn't there and John couldn't think of any smooth, charming lines to entice her to do what he wanted. All he could do was stall.

"Look. It's late. I've been on the road all day and I'm beat."

He saw her eyes flicker in confusion. She wasn't the only one who could weasel out of an argument by changing the subject abruptly.

"We can haggle over details in the morning," he said. "If you won't go. I'll stay. Tonight."

"Tonight?" she asked hoarsely. Her eyes were wide and suddenly unguarded. Her breasts rose and fell with her quickened breathing.

"Tonight," he repeated. "Come on. I'll help you lock up. We'll talk in the morning." He pushed to his feet. He shoved his hands into his pockets, more to keep from reaching out to touch her than for lack of anything to do with them.

"In the morning," she repeated weakly. "And then you'll go?"

"Hell, no. I'm on assignment, remember? The job says I have to protect you, Kelsey. It doesn't say a thing about you having to want me to."

Chapter 4

Thursday, November 11
7:30 a.m., Denver, Colorado

He found the smoker's corner in the Denver airport and leaned against the cinder block wall, staring out the dirty windows at the service area below. A light snow dusted the paving, made the planes white and ghostly. Bill drew on his cigarette, accepting the thick, gray clouds that delayed his flight with a calm, almost serene air.

He'd made it this far without detection, he didn't have to worry about such a minor detail like a snowstorm. If need be, he could rent a car and drive. He had cash, more now than he had last night, and he had a wide variety of credit cards to choose from. So far he'd only used the three females' cards, pulling the limit from three different automated teller machines in three different states. Somebody would trace them eventually, but it didn't matter; he'd already disposed of them in a trash bin in Philadelphia.

"Dr. Johnson?"

He turned, smiling. "Yes?"

"You asked me to let you know if there was any change in the ETA of your flight to Dallas. It's going to be another hour at least."

Bill blew out a cloud of smoke and allowed his smile to broaden. "Thanks for telling me, Angie. You're a wonder. Those airline people should snap you up. You're a lot friendlier than they are."

Angie giggled. "They tried. I make more in the beauty shop."

"I'll bet you do," he said. He sighed, without looking away from her. "I guess I'll just have to hang around a little longer." He let her understand he didn't mind this at all.

She smiled back. "An hour's not much time," she said, letting him know just how much she did comprehend.

"Oh, honey, in my line of work, an hour can be critical."

She giggled again and Bill put out his cigarette.

He didn't tip Angie, either. He didn't need to.

Thursday, November 11
8:00 a.m., Lubbock, Texas

Kelsey poured herself a cup of coffee, wrapping her cold hands around the mug to warm them. She tried shutting her ears to the sound of John's shower, tried closing her mind to the image of him standing beneath the water, rivulets streaming down his lean body.

He'd been in her house only twelve hours and had already managed to drive her practically crazy with his invasion. She hadn't slept well the night before, knowing he was only a wall away, all too able to picture him between the sheets, sprawled across the double bed that seemed too small for him.

Every time he'd moved, she'd heard him, had lain still upon her bed, tensed in some bizarre anticipation. But he hadn't reopened the bedroom door all night and hers had remained as firmly shut.

She wasn't used to sharing her house, her privacy, with anyone. She hadn't done so for three long years. And she wasn't sure she liked it now. It made her feel divided somehow, as though a part of her had to be listening for whatever the outside world might do to her, while, at the same time, part of her had to pay attention to the interior of her home. He destroyed her routine just by being there, and his being there destroyed her presence of mind.

The last thing he'd said before closing the door to the guest room was that they would come up with a plan in the morning. And all night long she'd tossed and turned thinking about the look on his face when he'd said it. Something in his expression gave her the feeling he hadn't been referring to Bill Winslow and her current predicament.

She'd asked how they could plan for something as vague as Bill Winslow's discovery of her whereabouts. He'd smiled tiredly and grazed her cheek with the back of his hand.

"Everything in life needs some kind of plan," he'd said.

She'd felt the blood rise to her cheeks and thought with a wild sort of desperation, whatever the reason John Chandler had come to her house, it wasn't strictly for her protection's sake. His words, the almost vowlike quality in his voice, gave him away. He had met her eyes steadily, a flash fire of some unexpressed emotion burning in the brown depths.

How could she stay alert to danger, when he distracted her so? And what was it about having him in her house that made her feel the greatest danger to her hard-won peace of mind was upstairs taking a shower?

The dim roar of the rushing water halted abruptly and she heard him whistling softly. She knew a moment's irritation with him. How dare he sound so cheerful? This was her life they were talking about, wasn't it? He sounded for all the world as though he was getting dressed for a Sunday picnic.

"Kelsey . . . ?"

She whirled around, having been so lost in her thoughts she hadn't heard him leave the bedroom and pad down the stairs.

"You move like a ghost," she snapped. But she wasn't angry over his having startled her, she was annoyed that he'd come down to the kitchen looking fresh, chipper and altogether too comfortable with this arrangement. She felt like something the cat dragged home, despite her own shower, in spite of the crisp, clean clothes she'd finally decided upon this morning.

His shirt was still half-undone, his broad chest still beaded with moisture that clung to the coarse brown curls. His hair was combed, his face smooth and sending off a hint of a clean, desert scent, but his feet were bare. A towel was still draped around his shoulders, apparently protecting the shirt from his still-wet hair or possibly from the shaving lotion.

Her knees felt strangely weak, and her fingertips actually tingled with reaction. She curled them into her suddenly warm palms, trying to subdue the urge to take the towel from his shoulders and brush it across his chest.

"Can I have a cup of that coffee?" he asked, pointing at the pot.

She stared at his finger blankly, followed its direction. He had the nerve to stand in her kitchen, still hot from the shower, a grin on his face, and ask for a cup of coffee?

Time seemed to fold in on itself. Last night, surrounded by shadows, lying in a darkened corner of her bedroom, too aware of the man in the next room, three years had seemed a lifetime. Suddenly in the harsh light of morning, his scent filling her nostrils, three years didn't seem a very long time at all.

"Kelsey?"

She met his eyes. She thought they might as well be touching, might as well be locked in an embrace, the unspoken message in his gaze was so clear. At the quickened pace of his breathing, his sudden stillness, the flicker in his eyes, she understood she must have been projecting equally strongly. She had the strange sensation of being in a vacuum, that all the air had disappeared.

She shook her head slowly; this couldn't be happening. She wasn't the same woman, no matter if he was totally the same man. After three years of carefully building a new life, no matter how it might be based on a foundation of lies, she had felt safe, secure. And the feelings he inspired in her were the first leap into chaos, for the minute she dropped her guard she would open herself up to a whole universe of hurt.

Whatever might have happened between them had died with her own rebirth. She knew, for all her wishes on twinkling stars, that she didn't have what it took to trust someone anymore. Bill had used every last bit of her trust, and a single kiss three years ago didn't mitigate it one little bit.

She set her own mug down, retrieved one for him and swiftly, sloppily, poured him a dollop of the dark brew. She set it on the counter and placed her palms facedown, cooling them against the Mexican tile, wishing they hadn't been shaking so noticeably, spelling out her reaction to him in graphic detail.

"I don't remember how you take it," she said deliberately, not looking at him, unwilling to put it in his hands herself. She picked up her own cup and held it in front of her like a tiny wet shield. She had to hold it with both hands.

"Hot," he said.

She felt a blush work a flash fire across her cheeks.

"Black's fine," he added. "I switched over years ago. It's too hard to take cream on a stakeout."

"I have cream," she said. Somehow the innocuous statement took on an alternate meaning, becoming an invitation of sorts. She hadn't intended it that way, had she? She risked a glance at him and was immediately sorry she had.

He was looking at her in a combination of curiosity and that stillness that presaged the feeling of a vacuum. His head was cocked slightly to one side and his full lips were unsmiling and thoughtful. His eyes seemed even darker than usual.

"I'm sure you do," he said. And like her words, his were filled with alternate possibilities.

She dragged her gaze free and drained her cup. Her hands felt even more unsteady as she poured another one. She was fully awake, all too alert, but felt as though she was still asleep and dreaming. John Chandler couldn't be standing so close to her that she could smell the scent of his shampoo and freshly applied after-shave, looking so at home, so at ease, so *there*.

"I've thought about it," he said, and she had the guilty feeling he was reading her mind. She glanced at him quickly and saw a glint of amusement in his eyes. "I've got a plan."

He moved to the dining table, hooked a chair with his bare foot. He straddled the chair backward, resting his elbows easily on the sturdy back. He swirled the coffee in the mug, staring down at it as if reading some message in the dark liquid. His jouncing right leg gave away some degree of his nervous energy. Or his tension. And somehow the sheer motion conjured other thoughts, inspired notions of other activities. Kelsey couldn't seem to look anywhere else but at that jostling leg. Her mouth felt dry and her mind numb.

"The way I see it," he said, cocking his head to one side— the unconscious gesture oddly sexy, "Winslow's first step was to shake the tails. The only reason he'd need to do that is because he *is* planning to find you. And since we know for a fact he saw that show, step two will be to track down that talk show to try and find out where your friend called from. I already called that Winters woman and told her not to spill the beans. She agreed. She also agreed to call the Bureau if anyone asked for that information.''

He nodded as if she had agreed with him.

''Think you can get your friend to keep low for a few days?'' he asked.

Kelsey shook her head.

''I think a little 'protective custody' might be in order for your lonely, confused gal.''

Kelsey couldn't help smiling. She could imagine how Jilly would react to that, like a greyhound to a well-seasoned steak.

''Well, we've got that on our side, then.''

With him sitting in her dining room, making her think all sorts of unruly things, that was the only thing she felt was on her side.

''But he's not stupid. He knows you're in Texas. And from what your friend said, he knows you're helping women somehow. He'll start with the phone books and then call those hot-line things saying he needs help or something. Are you in any directories?''

''For the training classes, yes. But under my assumed name,'' Kelsey said. ''And then only with a *K*. My home phone is unlisted.''

''Okay, good. But we can't lose sight of the fact that your ex is a con artist. For him, as determined as he seems to be, it shouldn't take too long to trace you. Are there any records out here in your own name?''

''No,'' she said. Her voice sounded cracked, as dry as her throat. She turned away slightly, concentrating on the refrigerator. Trying to concentrate on it, at any rate. How could he sit there, looking the way he did, talking so casually about something like Bill Winslow finding her?

But it wasn't the reference to Bill Winslow that was making her heart beat so uncomfortably, was it? Unfortunately the refrigerator didn't need washing.

She realized he was waiting for her to elaborate and swiftly sought the thread of their conversation. "I've always used Dobson."

"But stuck with the Kelsey?"

"That's standard policy," she said. "Seems a lot of people forget their new first name." She tried shooting him a look of scorn, but was sure it fell short of the mark.

"Okay. He's been out almost twenty-four hours now. One day for getting his bearings and shaking the tails and maybe digging up a little money. Another to get to Texas. Give or take a few hours. He can call the talk-show people from whatever airport he's flying in or out of, so that shouldn't slow him down any. My guess is he'll shoot for Dallas/Fort Worth first. It'll take him a while to settle on Lubbock."

She didn't say anything. He was right, that was exactly what Bill would do, and he was also right about Bill's being able to con the people involved into giving him whatever he wanted. Bill Winslow was a master at human manipulation. She should know. She'd given him house, hearth, savings accounts and all her love and trust besides. And what had he given her in return? Debts, former lovers, the back of his hand whenever she dared question him, and a contract on her life.

She turned to agree with John, to say his estimation of Bill's abilities was correct, and the words froze in her throat. John wasn't sitting at the table, a nice safe distance away from her. He was less than four inches away now.

She tried shrinking into herself, pulled back as far as she could, but she could still feel the heat radiating from his freshly scrubbed body, could smell his own scent beneath the splash of after-shave, could feel her skin tingling in sharp reaction.

He held up his mug. "I need another cup." He tipped the coffeepot—not spilling any—but he didn't return to his seat. He leaned against the bar instead, making her kitchen crowded and overly small.

"Are you hungry? Do you want something to eat?" Kelsey asked him nervously. *What exactly do you want, John Chandler?* she wanted to ask but couldn't.

John had to smile. This was so like the Kelsey he remembered, always having to do something. He'd watched her studying the icebox with assiduous care, and had been surprised she hadn't picked up the dish towel to swipe at it.

But she was as nervous as a school kid this morning. This would not be the first time today that she wouldn't meet his eyes, he noted. He was trying his damnedest to be casual, especially considering he felt anything but easy around her. When he'd heard her shower running, he'd realized his own would have to be cold for the most part. And trying to sleep in a room right next to hers had damn near driven him nuts. Every time she so much as rolled over, his mind supplied images of her perfect figure tangled up in those flowery sheets he'd glimpsed before they'd firmly shut their respective doors on possibility.

He swallowed a scalding gulp of his coffee and managed to say around his burning tongue, "So, I figure we'd better go into high gear, because he could be knocking on that door anytime after tonight. That is, if you still insist on staying here?"

"Yes," she said, and hoped it didn't sound as breathless to him as it did to her.

"I'll need the phone, then." Without waiting for an answer, he rounded the bar and lifted the receiver from the wall unit. Within seconds he'd barked orders to collect Jilly and keep her on ice, secure the Dallas/Fort Worth airport, fix teams to watch Kelsey's house on four-hour cycles, to patch through any calls from talk-show host Laurie Winters and to call Kelsey's home number the second they had any information as to Winslow's whereabouts or anything he may have done or anyplace he'd been in the past twenty-four hours. He hung up as abruptly as he'd begun the call.

"Now that we have a few things in place, and assuming he gets this far, we can figure out a plan of attack for once he gets here."

She looked up at him, startled into meeting his gaze. *"What?"*

"That's what you want, isn't it? To bag him?"

John felt a pang of guilt as she frowned over his question. This morning she was a lot closer to the Kelsey he used to know than the gun-toting woman of the night before. Maybe her toughness had been an act, put on for God only knew what reason.

"Or we could hustle you out right now, get you to a safe house," he added reasonably. Hopefully. A showdown with someone such as Winslow wasn't a good idea, but John wanted out of her house for a lot more reasons than that, the primary one being that everything about the place screamed Kelsey. He could smell that faint lemony scent in every room, could see her imprint on each object, every decorative touch in the place. A safe house would be just that...safer for John.

"No," she said swiftly. "No safe house. We've already been through that."

So, the act had been genuine enough, but why was she so nervous in the light of day? He'd smelled the coffee, heard her moving around and, like an animal following his nose, had made his way downstairs. And no matter how he tried acting calm himself, she remained jumpy, shaking hands clutching her coffee mug as if it were a talisman or shield, her shoulders drawn and pinched, her arms tight against her sides.

He'd tried to infuse a sense of purpose, tried to convey a certain blasé capableness, his ability to handle the job, keep her safe, an almost nonchalance about the danger facing her...facing them both. A sense that he could take care of anything, that he knew what to do next. And it wasn't an act. The only part he was faking was that he was immune to her. He was anything but.

Still, this was an assignment, and a damned dangerous one. They had to move quickly, had to operate swiftly, because Winslow was definitely on his way to find Kelsey. John had to know what she was capable of, how far that toughness went, and he had to know it fast. After her words the night before, the look on her set face, he'd assumed that she would welcome this matter-of-fact approach to the business at hand.

But instead of making her relax with the old Chandler tact, he'd just made her more nervous. He wanted to take that ridiculous coffee mug from her hands and warm them himself. He wanted to warm a lot more than that.

"Have you got a notepad or something I can write on?" John asked now, squelching whatever he might—and shouldn't—be feeling about Kelsey.

"In the highboy," she said, gesturing toward a large, Tao-styled pine chest that led the way into her spacious living room. He opened it and after staring at the contents in some surprise—it was a complete office system, computer and printer included—he found a spiral steno pad and pulled it free.

Before he could turn around, Kelsey asked, "Why you, John?" He froze at the question. He'd asked the same thing, but somehow, coming from her, the import seemed greater.

When she saw him stiffen, she realized she was holding her breath, waiting for an answer that seemed a long time in coming. She'd had to ask.

He didn't look at her as he mumbled, "I knew you. You knew me. The Bureau had to send someone you knew. Because of the Witness Protection guidelines."

"Damn the guidelines," she said softly. He turned to look at her then. She felt the shock of their locked gazes. This was a showdown of another variety. But it had to be said, had to be aired.

"They could have sent Charlie here," she suggested, not looking away from him now, needing to know the answer. What was she doing? Trying to get him to spell out how little he cared whether he had this assignment or not? What possible point was she trying to prove?

"Charlie's on his way to Peru," he said. A slight grin tugged at his lips. "To look for flying saucers."

She withheld an answering smile, perhaps in some measure of revenge for a too-offhand comment uttered so long ago. "Somehow that doesn't seem like Charlie."

"Apparently some of the UFO watchers dabble in more than aliens."

He had dodged what she was looking for with neat precision. She couldn't continue the line of questioning without sounding like an utter idiot.

She didn't have to. John answered, anyway, spelling it out with rough words totally at variance with his suddenly soft voice. "What do you want me to say, Kelsey? That they assigned me because they knew I'd kissed you three years ago? That I still want to? Hell, if they'd known that, they would have chosen any rookie rather than let me get within a hundred miles of you."

There was no way on earth she could have spoken. She was sorry she'd asked. And even sorrier that he'd admitted he still wanted to kiss her; it came too close to her own confused desires.

"I'm not proud of that kiss, Kelsey," he said slowly.

"But . . . ?" she asked, as much because he'd sounded as though there was a lot he was leaving out as because she truly wanted to know.

"All right," he said, accepting her challenge. "I'm not proud of it, *but* I'd do it again in one of Charlie's New York minutes."

Again Kelsey had that sensation of standing in a vacuum, all the air mysteriously having disappeared. She couldn't seem to breathe, couldn't seem to even think. She had totally misunderstood him just now. Her unintentional challenge had been met with a full body throw.

He slowly crossed the room, stopping in the doorway of the kitchen, blocking any hope of exit. It was unnecessary, she was sure she couldn't have moved if her life depended on it, and was just as certain that it somehow did.

He moved closer, and closer still until his shoulder brushed her hair, his knuckles grazed her upper thigh. But he didn't raise his hands or lean down. She had all but dared him to kiss her, she realized, and now couldn't tell if he meant to touch her or not. A rippling, eddying tingle radiated out from the contact points, dizzying her, making her feel strangely slow and torpid. She closed her eyes, praying for some kind of deliverance, but she couldn't have said what that might entail.

"Kelsey," he said softly.

When she didn't—wouldn't—look up, he lifted his hand to raise her chin so that she was forced to meet his gaze.

He was too close, she thought, and willed him to step back. When he didn't, when his bourbon brown eyes seemed to lure her deeper and deeper into their enmeshing gaze, she tried moving backward herself, but the refrigerator blocked her.

"Kelsey," he repeated. Her name on his lips was like the softest of touches, a promise of some kind, a caress. It undermined her determination not to lower her defenses, made her think of firesides and the taste of brandy on a hot tongue. Made her remember their one kiss, the kiss he'd said should never have happened.

"Please," she said more evenly than she felt, and only realized later she hadn't included a negative.

"Kelsey, don't be scared," he said.

She wanted to tell him he was the only thing making her nervous. But sheer nerves kept her lips sealed.

"We'll keep you safe."

Was that what he was talking about . . . Bill?

She half chuckled in relief, and a curious disappointment.

"What?" he asked.

"I thought . . . never mind."

"You thought what?"

Her heart was pounding so loudly she was certain he could hear it. "I thought you were going to kiss me," she mumbled.

She felt his stillness, the sudden tensing of the fingers against her jawline.

"If you only knew how much I wanted to," he said.

That tingling he'd inadvertently started by his touch now spread across her shoulders and down her spine. She met his gaze again, surprised, fearful . . . hopeful. She could see the sincerity in his gaze and it warmed her even as the confusion in his eyes surprised her. "Why?" she breathed.

He smiled, that one-sided, tug-of-the-lips grin that looked like a cross between devilry and confusion. "If you don't know, there's not a damn thing I can say to explain it."

She didn't say anything and he nodded as though he understood her thoughts.

"There aren't too many people in this world who could have gone through what you did and come out on the other side," he said slowly, changing the subject, or possibly following an alternate line of it. His fingers brushed against the fine hairs at the nape of her neck, sending a thousand shivers down her spine.

She tried thinking of those days in that bleak apartment, scared of her own shadow, frightened of even existing, and shook her head. But that didn't stop his torture.

"Sometimes I wonder if I am on the other side," she said. "Sometimes I don't even know what that means."

She was aware she was breathing too rapidly, that her entire being was focused on a pair of brown eyes, on the delicate touch of fingertips against her skin. That dreary morning seemed a thousand years in the past.

He didn't answer. His eyelids seemed to grow heavier, his gaze softened. His lips parted. She knew hers had, as well. Her limbs felt languorous and slow.

"I know what it means," he all but whispered, and his lips lowered to hers.

A shock wave of sensation ripped through her. His body was a magnet to hers and she could feel the sharp pull deep inside her. She told herself she should push him away, should do anything but continue to stand there, trembling, aching, but her mouth opened to draw him closer.

This couldn't happen, she thought incoherently. It wasn't in the cards. She couldn't allow herself even the merest brush with trusting someone again; she'd learned from sheer hard desperation exactly what trust meant.

And yet her lips molded to his, tasting him, yearning for more even as her mind spelled out their differences, the gulfs between them. He seemed to need no home, rolling from assignment to assignment, living out of suitcases; she craved stability with almost fanatic desperation. He believed in the strength, the sanctity of the law, the justice system; she knew it for a sham and distrusted everything about it.

And he was a man, and men hurt the women they cozened into believing them. Didn't they? Why couldn't she seem to understand that simple reality at this moment?

But thinking these things, *knowing* them, couldn't stop her heart from pounding, her fingers from numbing, her body from leaning into his. He tasted of the coffee she'd given him earlier, smelled of her soap and a touch of his after-shave. His touch was gentle and firm at the same time and made her remember, made her want to forget.

As slowly as the morning sun rose in the east, he raised his head and pulled at the air as though he were suffocating. She allowed herself the respite of resting her cheek against his shoulder, gasping for air herself.

"Ah, Kelsey," he murmured against her hair. His tone was sad, lonely. It made her want to cry.

Neither of them moved for several seconds. It seemed like lifetimes. She'd forgotten what simply being held could mean. How long had it been since she'd given in to the comfort of a hug, warm arms embracing her, holding her tightly against a broad chest? Since the last time John Chandler had held her, kissed her that one and only time three years earlier.

She stiffened and pulled back from him, not daring to meet his gaze. If she did, she would be lost in the depths of his brown eyes. Not forever, maybe not even for long, but lost nonetheless. She felt disoriented now. And she was all too conscious of missing her ever-present anger, that it had been supplanted by nostalgia, by mystery, by confusion. And most of all, by a longing so intense she felt shattered. If one kiss could do that to her, what would happen if she gave in again, if she looked up and allowed him to glimpse the hunger in her?

She desperately sought her sustaining anger, her life force, the source of her strength.

"I'm not the same woman I was," she said more harshly than she intended, her eyes on the floor.

"I'm not the same man," he countered easily. Too easily, she thought. She risked a glance at his face. His features were etched with unspoken emotion, but what emotions those might be she couldn't begin to guess.

"I'm not married anymore," he added softly.

Was that an explanation for the kiss, an oblique apology for the one years before, or was he implying that his single status made everything okay now? It wasn't okay. His being divorced, widowed, or whatever he was, was only a fact of life, not a factor in whether or not she would ever succumb to another such kiss.

She smiled half-bitterly. "I'm not a victim anymore," she countered.

"I can see that," he said. He trailed the edge of his thumb along the curve of her cheek. A shiver followed in its wake, and goose bumps prickled on her arms. She wanted to tell him to go to hell and beg him to continue his touch all at the same time. She shifted her head away from that seductive contact.

"I wasn't kidding, John, when I said the Kelsey you knew was dead. I did die three years ago. And when I was born again, I had a new life, a new last name, and I found the only thing that really matters is anger."

"That's not true, Kelsey."

"It is for me."

"No one could change that much," he said.

"I did," she said calmly, coldly.

He dropped his hands from her slowly, and stepped back a pace. He leaned against the edge of the kitchen wall. He looked so natural there, she wanted to tell him to move. It's my wall, my house, my life, even *my* loneliness...don't come in here and confuse me, she wanted to say, ached to say. But saying the words aloud would grant them greater import than a single—a second kiss in three years deserved.

"Why?" he asked, confusing her. For a moment she actually wondered if he'd read her mind. "Why is anger the only thing that really matters?"

For John, still trapped as he was in the sweet taste of her lips, the moment seemed almost unbearably poignant. He leaned against the wall as much to detain her a moment longer as to support his back. She had disarmed him when she'd said she sometimes didn't known what being on the other side of a broken life even meant.

He wished she could know how much he admired her and how much he wanted to kiss her again, feel her body against his. He hadn't even known just how much himself until he heard the words spilling from his lips. They hadn't come from his mind, he discovered; they had come from some part of him that he seldom set free. It didn't come from mere desire, it was much more complex than that. Perhaps it had come from that part of him that knew the cutting edge of courage.

He should never have accepted this assignment, should never have kissed her, should never have even *touched* her. There was something about Kelsey that got under his skin. Like a disease, he told himself, but knew he was lying. If that were a disease, people would line up to catch it.

If only she weren't so beautiful, so achingly vulnerable despite her tough act, the gun, the cold voice. And, he thought suddenly, if only he'd met her years ago, long before he discovered that when hearts broke, they never really mended.

She studied him for a long moment, almost as if he were some rare and particularly nasty variety of insect. What had he asked her? He couldn't remember. Something about why she felt anger.

"Necessity," she said. "I learned that anger is the only thing that matters through sheer necessity."

"Necessity is simply getting through the days till the heat dies down," he said, trying to feel his way through the sudden conviction that the ground he stood on was land mined.

Her eyes flashed. "And when might that be, John? When is the heat going to end? You told me it was over three years ago. So when is it going to stop? When hell freezes over?"

John couldn't think of any retort to that one and knew it didn't matter because it was strictly a rhetorical question.

"You know I'm right. Bill made that perfectly clear when they were taking him away. You heard him. I would *never* be safe from him, remember? And you believe that. So does the FBI. Or you wouldn't be here. So you see, fear, vulnerability, trust, all those things aren't going to help me one whit. Anger will."

"Not anger, Kelsey. Maybe—"

She pushed away from the bar, from him, sprang from her stance like a pilot ejected from a burning plane. "Maybe nothing!" she snapped. "You don't know the half of it!"

"I know a lot more than you might think," he said, thinking of that diary tucked in his overnighter upstairs. "And I know that arguing about it isn't going to help anything. We have to get organized."

"I was organized before you got here," she blurted out.

He frowned a question. She didn't answer, and for some reason she blushed. He didn't have the foggiest notion why she'd done it, but it proved she wasn't lashing out at him for anything he'd done in the past, not even for the kiss they'd just shared, but for something in her head, something that had to do with his sheer presence. The notion didn't necessarily displease him.

"Your life may have been organized, but there are things we need to do here, set up some basic protective measures. You heard me setting up the observe teams. They're probably already in place, or will be relieving the team that watched last night. Everything is set. Now all we have to do is hook up the alarms, set up the tracer—in case he calls—and see what you can do in the way of defending yourself."

He moved out of the kitchen and back to the table. "Then we just sit back and wait." He looked up at her and smiled.

She gazed back with a guarded, suspicious expression.

He nodded, as though they'd made some agreement, then picked up the notepad. Almost as an afterthought, which it certainly wasn't, he added, "But the object is to collar Winslow. And that's it. Got it?"

Charlie was right: charm was definitely his weak suit. She didn't say anything.

He turned and met her gaze. "Agreed?"

She still didn't speak. Her lips were compressed into a thin line that strangely didn't detract from her appeal but somehow enhanced it.

"Agreed, Kelsey?" he repeated, adding her name, compelling her to answer him in the affirmative. When she remained silent, her eyes sliding away, he said, "With what we know about him in prison, what he said and his shaking the tails, if he shows up here this time, we'll be more than able to prove to any judge what he's capable of. They'll lock him up and throw away the key."

"All I have is cereal. Is that okay?"

John had to blink at the abrupt change of subject. And he hated cereal. He was a bacon- or steak-and-eggs man. And she was avoiding the issue. She was pulling the same trick on him he'd used on her the night before, that she'd used on him before that.

"Cereal's fine," he said in his best imitation of enthusiasm. Eating rabbit food was just punishment for trying to force her to see reality so early in the day. Or was it punishment for the kiss she'd obviously enjoyed every bit as much as he had? If it was punishment, it was mighty excessive.

"Cream or milk?" she asked.

He smiled. Maybe she wasn't all that uncomfortable, he thought. "Oh . . . *cream,*" he said slowly, deliberately, waiting for her to look at him.

Chapter 5

Kelsey felt the blush painfully burn her cheeks, her neck. She thought, rather incoherently, that John's smile was one of his best features, and even as she felt her own lips curve in response, she tried resolutely hardening her heart against him. He seemed intent on teasing her this morning. It didn't seem right that he should do so. It smacked of an intimacy that didn't exist between them. It made her want to lower her ever-present guard.

"So, what is your plan, besides waiting?" she asked, setting a bowl on the counter and filling it with chunks of granola and raisins. She liberally splashed cream over the cereal, taking some pleasure at the sharp look of distaste on his face. Two could play at teasing, she thought, and only later realized how easily she'd succumbed to his assumption of intimacy.

She picked up a dishrag and swiped at the counter almost angrily. She looked up to find him grinning again. She wished she understood that smile, wished it didn't conjure so few memories, so many different yearnings.

"That's the plan. Just wait." He spooned a mouthful of granola into his mouth and chewed it slowly, his expression one of sharp distaste.

"Can't we just go public and get him here sooner?"

"Or scare him off," he said after swallowing with a grimace. "I thought of that last night. But it doesn't wash, because if we scare him off, he might wait six months, or even a year and come around when we're not ready for him."

Kelsey withheld a shiver at the thought. She was also aware of the mistaken pronoun he'd used—*we*. If they scared him off now, she would either be alone or having had to start over somewhere else. Either way it would be a Kelsey-loses-again scenario.

She couldn't help but feel a little sorry for John trying to down a breakfast he obviously hated, though she'd have to remember that, then reminded herself that it wouldn't matter, a few days, a week, and he'd be gone. She hardened her heart. She hadn't asked him here. "And what will happen?"

"We'll get him."

"No, I mean afterward. He'll come here, you'll nab him, and if he doesn't kill me—or shoot at one of you guys—he'll get slapped on the wrist for violating the standing restraining order. And he'll come back. What then, John?" When he only looked at her, she asked more pointedly, "What happens then?"

"We'll get him again."

"And then what? Another move, another town, another death, another life to start all over again? Or will it be a case of third time's the charm for Bill, that he'll finally get me?"

"We'll get him," he said calmly.

Kelsey sighed. Three years ago she'd hung on John's every assurance. Now she knew all too well what those assurances were worth.

"Not unless you *really* get him. Not unless he's not going to be around to ever come back again," she said.

John just looked at her. There it was again, that dark threat in her voice. He ached to tell her he understood. How could he not? He'd thought the same thing a thousand times himself. Anyone in his business had. But it wasn't the same; they *had* to play it by the rules.

"If you don't plan to get rid of him once and for all, there's nothing you can do for me, John. Get in your car and go on back to your wife. I can take care of myself now."

"I'm not married anymore, remember?" he said, as if that was the only important thing to tell her.

Her back stiffened. "Oh, that's right. I'm sorry."

"I'm not," he said equally stiffly.

She didn't say anything and John wondered if she was mulling over the implications in what he'd said. "We'll get him, Kelsey," he said finally. "It's only a matter of time."

Her eyes blazed at him. "And it'll only be a matter of time until he's out again and coming after me again. No, John. Running isn't the answer. Staging my death isn't the answer. Not this time. Not ever again. As they say in the old Westerns, this world ain't big enough for the two of us. It's him or me. That's the only way to end this once and for all. And, I'll tell you something, I'm putting my money in my corner."

John stared at her, drank in her determination, her anger, the implacable stance, the no-guts-no-glory attitude, and had to bite back a hearty good-for-you. What she wanted was against the law, the law he was sworn to uphold.

"Okay," he said, not saying anything really.

Surely she knew he wasn't going to walk away. She could try driving him off all she wanted, but it wasn't going to work. And he wasn't about to hand her over to some other agent, although a part of him half wanted to. But that part wasn't the agent half of him, it was only the man beneath.

However, there was no way he could accept her him-or-me attitude. But with time—and he had precious little of that—he might be able to talk some reason into her.

The trouble was, using a hellish sort of logic, she made perfect sense. She was right. With a man like Winslow, it would always be just a matter of time until he was free to come and kill her. In the meantime he could haunt her every waking moment.

John's very nature wanted to applaud her, wanted to grab her tense, shaking shoulders and whirl her around in some mad triumphant dance. You're right, he wanted to yell. Let's get the bastard. It would be justice at its most extreme. Only the problem with extreme justice was that it bred extreme *in*justice.

But aside from her all-or-nothing attitude, John was feeling an irrational stab of jealousy. All the passion in Kelsey was being expended on her worthless, hell-bent husband. Not on one hardened, never-get-involved agent who was still reeling from a single taste of her.

"Okay, Kelsey. Have it your way. Keep your damned anger. Feed it if you have to. Whatever it takes. But I'm staying here with you. And we're going to nab Winslow my way."

"No."

"Yes. There are no options here. This isn't a gestalt session. This is martial law. And you have to live by the rules."

"This is my house, therefore we're going to live by *my* rules," she said almost truculently.

He smiled. He couldn't help it. "You're right, it's your house," he said, not agreeing to her calling the shots, but to the ownership of her home.

"You'd agree to that?"

"Yes." How could he not? It *was* her house.

"Why?"

Come on, John, he thought. For once in your life, pull some razzle-dazzle out of your hat. But he couldn't, it simply wasn't in him. "Because, Kelsey, while I sure don't agree with your him-or-me attitude, I have to admit, Winslow's a wild card. He doesn't fit any hole the system can find for him."

He noted the glimmer of triumph in her eye and continued without pause. "However, that system's all we've got. And as long as I can draw breath, we're going to play by the law."

"It's the very law you love so much that lets a man like Bill get away with the things he does."

John couldn't help raising his hand to his forehead. He wanted to shake some reason into her, wished she didn't make so much sense. "It's not that simple, Kelsey. Nothing is black-and-white. There's shades of gray. You can't simply dismiss the law as if it were an inconvenient evil."

"Why not? Bill did."

"And he went to prison for it."

"But he's out now, isn't he? And we both know what he wants."

"You," John said. And the minute the word came out of his mouth, John knew that in one very real respect he was like Bill Winslow. He, too, wanted Kelsey. Badly. But in a very different way.

"You're here to guarantee he's not going to succeed this time?"

Hell. There weren't any guarantees. But he felt she'd definitely challenged everything he stood for, everything he was, so he couldn't exactly say that. Instead he said, "He didn't pull it off last time, honey. Remember?"

She shrugged, the consummate tough cookie under fire. Somehow instead of appearing nonchalant, insouciant, all she looked was plain old scared. John wanted to reach across and grab her, pull her into his arms and cradle her. But he didn't. He couldn't. He'd comforted her once and damn near drowned in her need. And in the ache she inspired in him.

But it seemed to him now that, in her eyes, it must have seemed he had walked out on her. She was as much a product of his making as that of the justice system or her horror of an ex-husband. He had led her to expect that she could lean on him, could *trust* him. And she must have believed he'd simply used her, kissed her like some woman-in-every-port jerk.

And he'd done it again. Kissed her and then turned abruptly to business. What kind of a guy was he? He didn't think he wanted an answer to that.

Because the truth was, he'd run from her. And he still wanted to run, as far and as fast as he could go. For she still reminded him of things he'd really never known, things such as honor and responsibility, those intangible somethings that spelled home and honesty and involvement. Things that comprised need, things that would complicate his life and make him feel he would let her down again.

She sighed and turned away from him as if she'd been reading his mind. Her head bent, and he was pierced by the very loneliness of her stance. Was she crying? Her arms lifted and wrapped around her chest, as though she were hugging herself.

"I'm sorry, Kelsey," he said. And he felt he was apologizing for far more than a mistaken kiss three years ago, than having admitted he still wanted her. He was apologizing for Bill Winslow, for every time the man had lied to her, stolen from her, used the back of his hand to teach her a lesson.

"I'm sorrier than I can say." And at this, he wasn't sure if he was apologizing for what she'd had to live through or for being a "sorry" excuse for a rescue. He went on swiftly, "But I'm here for you."

Her silence lent his words greater import than he might have intended. They echoed in his own ears, forcing him to

realize that for once in his life he was actually asking someone to let him be involved. The thought scared the living
daylights out of him. He wished he could modify the offer,
retract it somehow.

"You don't owe me anything," she said. Her voice was
low and muffled.

"You're wrong, Kelsey."

"What do you owe me?" she asked.

"I owe you the truth," he said. And suddenly he knew
they weren't talking about Winslow anymore.

"And what's that?"

John felt the future was rushing at him, that the past was
slamming him with the force of a crashing jet plane. There
were too many realizations coming too fast, too hard.

"You don't have to answer," she said, and by saying it,
demanded one anyway.

Had he gone nuts? He'd asked for this. What on earth
was it about her that made him lose sight of the job, the
case? But damn it, it was her *life* they were arguing about.
Maybe if she heard the truth about what he'd felt, what he'd
thought three years ago, maybe then she'd give him that
modicum of trust he needed to keep her alive.

"After I kissed you that night three years ago... I was
scared spitless. It didn't have anything to do with Dayna.
That was on the rocks, anyway. It had to do with me. I ran."

She was silent so long John was hoping he'd only imagined saying the words. And when she did finally answer,
John felt as if she'd jerked the chair out from under him,
spilling him onto the floor and further. Far below.

"Well, I guess one good truth deserves another. I was
more than halfway to falling for you, John."

John pushed away from the bar, knowing that nothing on
earth could keep him from her now. The gritty feel of the
cereal against his teeth disappeared, the pain in his back was
suddenly and miraculously gone. The past receded and an

entirely new present unfolded before him. He stepped around the bar, reaching for her.

She turned before he could take her into his arms. The look in her eyes, her next words, stopped him cold. "But that was three years ago. As the young kids say, that was then, and this is now."

If there had been tears in her eyes before, they were absent now. Her hot blue gaze met his. "I'm a different person now, John."

"The fundamental beliefs can't change," he said hoarsely. He'd never wanted to believe anything so much in all his life.

"They can, too," she said. "And I have. If you can live with that . . . you can stay."

"And if I said I couldn't live with that?"

"I'd say don't let the door hit you on your way out and write if you get work."

Her words, the look on her face should have wounded him. He knew that was her intention, her purpose behind them. Instead, as her anger had the night before, they only served to rouse his own anger. He wasn't the kind of man who took it on the chin with a grin and a shrug. And his anger wasn't something he often dodged.

Everything about this new Kelsey, her stiffness, her coldness, her obsession with her former husband, her callous dismissal of his heartfelt confession, they all conspired to fire him up in a way he hadn't experienced in years. What he was feeling now made his last night's anger seem like intermission at a Sunday school dance.

He stepped forward. She didn't flinch at all. She challenged him with her eyes, her defiance. He moved closer and closer, not threatening, merely promising. When he was less than a hand-span's width from her, he stopped. He forced her gaze to remain with him, and slowly, achingly slowly, he held out his hand.

She glanced down at the outstretched palm almost fearfully.

"What am I agreeing to?" she rasped.

"You don't trust anything, do you, Kelsey?" he asked, leaving his hand between them. He wanted to drive her to her knees, to make her beg for his protection; he wanted to do anything to make her sorry for having made him all but plea for letting him get involved in her life, for wanting her in his, however briefly it would have to be.

But he was no Winslow. And even if he was mad enough to shove his fist through the nearest cinder block wall, he would never *ever* take it out on a woman, especially Kelsey.

He repeated his question slowly. "Do you, Kelsey? Trust anything?"

"Not anything, or any*one*," she answered finally.

"Fair enough. Neither do I."

"So, what am I agreeing to?" she asked again, her voice stronger this time, sultry now, steady.

"The cold-bloodiest partnership in history," he answered.

His hand still stretched between them. He wished angrily that she would just take it so he could pump it furiously and let her go. More than that, however, he wished he could just drag her into his arms and kiss her senseless.

"And what does that mean, exactly?" she asked. He would have thought her calm, except for the telltale pulse in her throat.

"I mean that you're going to have to trust somebody. You're going to have to trust *me*. I mean that we're going to stay here, work together, try not to kill each other in the process...and we're going to nail Winslow. Once and for all."

She searched his eyes for a long moment, trying, he thought, to find a modicum of truth, a measure of something she could trust, then he felt her cold hand slip into his.

"John Chandler...you've got yourself a deal."

And as she returned the pressure of his hand, he suddenly didn't feel angry anymore. But he devoutly wished he did.

Upstairs, away from him, trying to feel some sense of her own presence in the house that no longer seemed quite hers, Kelsey wondered if she wasn't dreaming. Nothing in the past twenty-four hours had seemed real.

One minute she'd been standing outside her back door, gazing at the stars and wishing for a richer life, and the next, FBI agent John Chandler had knocked on her door, moved into her house, kissed her mindless and offered her the bargain of a lifetime.

He was going to stay. The rest of the bargain didn't seem to really matter, he'd offered her *himself.* What more could a person ask?

That all depended, she thought, with her now customary caution, on what that offer really meant. Lots, she decided. His staying in a place didn't mean safety for her, didn't necessarily confer security. Conscious of the need to subjugate some of her thoughts, she resolved that as of this minute she'd have to regard him as an extra mouth to feed, an extra load of laundry, another detriment to a peaceful night's sleep—for myriad reasons.

If she was honest with herself, which she had to be in these bizarre circumstances, she wasn't at all eager to see him leave. And she had to admit this, knowing what he did to her insides.

On the plus side, there was a lot of truth in the adage about safety in numbers and if she had a number to choose from, John's would be it. He was the consummate FBI agent—tough, resilient, capable. He was not only bright, he was remarkably fast on his feet and, perhaps more important, a very handy man with a weapon.

She'd gone through extensive training, but John was a specialist. She'd spent the past couple of years training other victimized women on how to spot a potential Mr. Wrong, whereas John arrested the bad guys of the world. Essentially, she was a prepared amateur while he was a professional.

So having his help was a good thing.

On the surface.

On the minus side, there was entirely too much beneath that thin-skinned covering that made up her life. She couldn't pretend that when he'd kissed her she'd pulled back, rejecting him. That wasn't how it had been at all. Three years ago, or now.

She had kissed him in return. Had kissed him as if there was no tomorrow, as if yesterday had been a mere prelude to passion, as if the present were endless.

She wished she could tell herself that it was simply a matter of being lonely for so long, that loneliness had become a natural state of affairs and that a single kiss, a single embrace by any man, would have made her turn to pure jelly. But it wasn't true. Not in John's case. Not in hers.

The truth was much more complex than that. He'd been the last man to hold her, the last man, perhaps the only one, with whom she felt safe. And she'd responded to him, then, and even more so now, with all the pent-up craving of anyone who had gone through a life-changing transformation.

She had told him she was different, and so she was. But she wasn't altogether a different person. He had been right when he'd said the fundamental values couldn't change. Was that why she had responded to him, because he was right and fundamentally she was the same? Or was it simply propinquity? Or was it that he was probably one of the few people on earth who knew her real name?

It was all of those things, she thought sadly. And more.

She could hear him now, downstairs, glued to the telephone, scribbling notes on the pad he'd found what seemed days earlier in her highboy. Had it only been an hour ago that he'd held her in his arms, making her want too many things she couldn't even name anymore?

She'd gone upstairs when he'd first picked up the telephone, thinking to give him privacy, wishing to be away from his sheer male presence for a while. And she'd found herself in his room—*her* guest room—trying to sort out her scattered feelings. It didn't help. He might as well have been in the room. She could *feel* him, could smell his unique and utterly enticing scent, could almost taste him.

He was untidy. She'd forgotten that small detail if she'd ever noticed it. She picked up his previous day's clothing, which he'd dropped to the floor. Folding them, she couldn't resist pressing her face to the back of his shirt. If any chemist ever replicated that exact scent, there wouldn't be a woman on earth who could resist buying a bottle of it for her mate, she thought a little wildly.

She set his things down on the chair near the window, tried thinking of them as merely clothing, covering, but saw them on him all too easily, saw them discarded even more easily.

He'd wadded the washcloth on the side of the sink of the small guest bathroom. It, too, carried the scent of him, the scent of her soap, her shampoo. After holding it to her face, feeling like a teenager with hormones going berserk, she primly folded the cloth and draped it over the side rail.

She felt as if she were prying into the secret life of John Chandler, touching the things he'd worn, the items he'd touched, the socks, the pants, the soap he'd pressed to his skin. The intimacy of the inanimate articles made her feel awkward, and at the same time made her feel pleasantly languid.

She wondered if he might feel the same way staying in her house. Would he even think in that fashion? It seemed unlikely. He was too much the tough agent, the man on the road, the lone stranger who would always find a way to ride off into the sunset rather than find a place to hang that white hat the good guys always wore.

She pulled the covers of the bed into place and bent to retrieve his overnight bag. She told herself later that she hadn't intended to look inside, that she'd inadvertently picked the bag up by one handle and in doing so, had accidentally spilled some of the contents to the plush carpet.

Luckily the carpet *was* thick, she thought, swiftly grabbing the slim laptop computer and setting it carefully back into the bag. Another plastic and metal electronic device had spilled free, also, and she placed it atop the computer. Clean socks, a spy novel, and a hard-bound journal were all that remained on the floor. She put away the socks and the novel and was absently reaching for the journal when she recognized the handwriting on the front of it.

An icy chill spread through her veins. A knot formed in the pit of her stomach. A journal with Bill's handwriting on it. What was John doing with Bill Winslow's journal in his overnighter?

Slowly, feeling her heart beginning to pound in even slower painful beats, she straightened. She held the journal in one hand, lifted his overnighter with the other. She set his bag down on the desk and because her legs felt suddenly weak, took the desk chair for herself.

Opening the journal to the first page, she started reading. She had to read the first few paragraphs over twice before her eyes would allow the meaning to sink into her mind. She turned the pages, one after another, feeling herself grow colder by the word, sicker by the phrase. She had to cover her mouth to keep a pitiful moan locked inside.

She thought she'd known the worst about Bill Winslow. She'd been cheated by him, abused by him both physically and mentally. He'd even hired someone to kill her, had valued her life at only ten thousand dollars. But this, this outpouring of a diseased mind, this was worse than anything she could ever have imagined.

In this journal, in this literary rival of anything the Marquis de Sade might have penned, Bill had described in graphic detail the various tortures he would subject her to, if he ever found her. *When* he found her.

"We've got trouble," John said from the hallway.

She looked up dully and watched him round the doorjamb, step into the room.

"Winslow's left a..." he trailed off, stopping. Assessing.

If he'd come into the room fifteen minutes earlier, she would have whirled in embarrassment for having been caught in his quarters, touching his things, drinking in his scent. But she had read the journal now.

John's eyes narrowed as he took in what she held in her numb hands. "Oh, God, Kelsey, I didn't want you to see that."

She tried understanding his words, but they seemed to be coming from somewhere far away, some other planet maybe.

She scarcely saw him move, he crossed the room so swiftly. He plucked the journal from her hands and tossed it in the direction of his overnighter. He took her cold, cold hands in his. He knelt beside her, his legs on either side of hers like a shield, like a solid wall of warmth.

"Look at me, Kelsey."

Apathetically, she did as he asked.

"Now listen." He drew a deep breath before proceeding. "That diary doesn't change anything."

She wanted to believe him. She clung to his gaze as if she would drown without the lifeline his eyes were offering.

"It's just words. The words of a sick man. You're strong, Kelsey. Stronger than any woman I know. He can't touch you now, you said it yourself, you've put your money in your corner. I would too. My money's on you. Now, forget about that diary. Let it go. It's only evidence, that's all. Just another piece of material the D.A. will use to lock him up and throw away the key.''

''Really?''

''Really, Kelsey.''

''I mean, you'd really put your money in my corner?''

''I already have,'' he said. ''I'm here.''

John smiled, relaxed his tight grip on her fingers. She was amazed to feel them now when moments earlier she'd felt as though she was only trying to make contact. *I'm here,* he'd said. Yes, he was. However temporarily. She returned the pressure of his fingers and his smile broadened, the hard line of his jaw softening somewhat.

He rested his arms on her legs, not releasing her hands. He looked up at her with an are-you-all-right-now question in his eyes. She didn't know the answer. She wasn't sure she *was* all right.

Everything was *not* all better now. Seeing Bill's hatred for her spelled out in black and white, having John leaning against her, asking her to lean on him, telling her that all that vitriol amounted to was evidence against Bill, somehow all conspired to make her feel snared in the past.

She tried seeing from John's perspective and found that too daunting. All the journal represented to him was a little dragon in his knight errantry. See, honey? It's just a little bitty old thing, and can't hurt you. Nothing to be scared about. John could look at it that way, could really believe it, because this was only a job to him, not his *life.* It wasn't his body Bill had carved up so lovingly in those pages, it wasn't his mind that Bill wanted to destroy. Those words, the careful construction of the details, the promises, the threats, worked to steal the past three years of a new life away from her. And John was trying to tell her that it wasn't important, that it didn't matter. Of course, it mattered.

And it mattered that he was straddling her, open to her in all ways but emotionally, protecting her with his body if not his heart. That this was unfair, she couldn't admit right then. Because she didn't dare admit that she needed him right now, wanted him to play the knight, hold her in his arms and murmur pretty lies that everything would be okay, that he would take care of everything for her. And she didn't dare acknowledge how much such empty promises would mean at this particular moment.

She asked him how he came by the journal and he told her.

"Did the parole board see this journal?" she asked after a long pause.

He hesitated, then nodded.

"Then how could they release him?" she asked.

He shook his head, looking miserable. "I don't know, Kelsey. I wasn't in on the decision. The Bureau forwarded our recommendation, but I guess that didn't count for much."

She felt a notch of the tension ease from her shoulders. Why should it matter so much that the FBI had tried to intercede on her behalf, or at the very least, had tried keeping Bill behind bars? She didn't know why, she only knew that it did.

If Kelsey had any idea of how much he wanted to take her into his arms right now, John thought, she'd probably slap him. And she'd be right to do so.

When he'd stepped into that room and saw her holding that damnable diary, all the color gone from her face, her eyes large with shock and pain, he hadn't even thought, he'd just gone to her.

He wished he weren't on assignment, wished he wasn't a so-called peace officer. He wanted to rip Bill Winslow into a million pieces with his bare hands. He wanted to shoot the man down, empty his gun into him and stand there and watch the life draining from him, the poison spilling from his body.

And he wanted to take Kelsey into his arms, kiss her until her skin flushed with dewy luster, love her until she forgot

Winslow's hatred, couldn't think of anything but him, couldn't want anything but his touch, his lips.

He wanted her to touch him back, to still the anger in him, to steal the fear that had always been his guard with her, with everyone. And he wanted a respite, a breather from thinking about every detail of this assignment. Because if he slipped up on this one, Kelsey would be dead, and that he couldn't bear to think about.

He'd come upstairs looking for her to tell her they had trouble. Bill Winslow hadn't merely shaken his FBI tails, he'd left a trail of mayhem behind him as he went. At this point, they had no proof—no concrete proof, anyway—that it *was* Winslow who had killed a medical supplies salesman in West Virginia, or the physician the salesman was visiting that day. But the FBI did know that someone had used a cocktail waitress's credit card in Philadelphia, and that the man who had apparently taken it from her purse fit Winslow's description.

And they did know that someone had killed a beautician in the back room of a beauty shop in Denver after she'd apparently conducted a dye job in the early morning hours. All the money was gone from the safe, though the investigating agent doubted the owner's estimate of the amount of cash in the storage compartment.

Then there was a Dr. Johnson—the same name as that of the murdered physician's—who had boarded a plane from Denver to Dallas/Fort Worth. A check of all hotel registers was under way now, but those were both big cities and the information could take hours to collect. There was also no guarantee that Winslow would still be using the doctor's name.

He could have told her all this a few minutes ago. He would have. But she had read that damned diary and tough-cookie Kelsey had been lost in those pages.

John thought if he had anything specific to hate Winslow for, it was this, stripping Kelsey of her hard-won fierceness. She'd earned it at a very hard school and John would be damned if anyone was going to steal it from her now.

Lifting a hand to her chin, he made her look directly at him. Her eyes seemed lost, confused. Too many hurts, too much of a life spent running from Bill Winslow. Her face was pale and her lips trembled.

Touching her at all had been a mistake. Her extreme vulnerability tugged too sharply at him, made him want to give her comfort—and more. Meeting her troubled gaze made him wonder if he could work to rouse the anger so necessary to her now.

"It'll be all right," he said. He'd told her this before and thought the words lame back then. They were equally ineffective today.

Her lips moved slightly, as if she were framing some question. Her eyes, still linked with his, asked a thousand questions, all of them painful. He couldn't stand to see this.

"Damn it, Kelsey," he muttered. "This shouldn't be happening." Even as the words left his mouth, they surprised him. Had he meant that Bill Winslow shouldn't be chasing her, or that he, John, shouldn't be wanting to kiss her again? Kiss her until he'd erased all memory of Winslow and his terrible hatred.

As if reading his mind, she leaned forward, close enough that he could feel her warm breath, could drink in that delicate lemony scent.

"You don't hate me, do you, John?" she whispered. It wasn't an invitation. It was the heartbreaking question of a woman who had been used too harshly, treated to terror instead of love.

"No, hating you would be impossible," he said, and knew he meant that with every fiber of his being. Hating Kelsey would be a contradiction of terms, a physical, emotional impossibility.

He should have pulled back. He knew that, but realized, at the same time, that he was incapable of such heroism. There were limits to a man's nobility. Kelsey leaning into him was perhaps the most severe test of his determination to remain at arm's length. A test he reluctantly, but gladly, failed as he raised his lips to hers.

She trembled for a moment, seeming to hesitate even as she pressed against him. Swiftly, her arms encircled his shoulders and she slid from the chair into his welcoming embrace.

"God, what you do to me," he growled. Raking his hands through her hair, he swept them down her back, pulling her sharply against him. Taking her slight weight against him fully, he straddled her, letting her slide down to rest in the V between his legs. Kneeling now, fiercely crushing her to him, demanding that she eradicate her fear, needing her to think of him, not Winslow, John gave in to the kiss, unable to stop, unable to listen to the inner alarm bells screaming at him.

She responded to him with an almost desperate intensity. And while he'd wanted her to forget Winslow, had, in some complicated subconscious way, wanted to be the instrument of that amnesia, he found he didn't particularly like this new role. How would Kelsey look at this breach of confidence when she *wasn't* feeling frightened? How would he?

She'd never know how reluctantly he pulled himself away. She would never know, and he'd certainly never tell her, that he was trembling so much he was literally shaking inside. But Kelsey needed his strength, not his desire. She needed her anger back, not his kisses.

He hid his desire, his confusion over what the kiss had done to him. "Better now?" he asked, hating himself for the callous tone, but doing it deliberately.

As he'd feared, her eyes seemed to flatten, the soft light in them fading too swiftly to indicate anything but hurt. But as he'd hoped—planned—that softness was soon replaced with a bright blaze of pure fury.

"What happened to that anger you told me you're eating for breakfast?" he chided, holding her at arm's length.

Swiftly, he pushed to his feet. He dusted his pant legs as if nothing extraordinary had occurred. If he were to meet her eyes now, she'd see the lie, see how much he'd been affected by her kiss, by her need.

"I don't care if you'd rather sit here and mope about some words scrawled in a notebook, but it seems to me we've got better things to do with our time," he said, turning his back on her.

He heard her sharp intake of anger.

"So, if you've had enough whining about this, can we get back to work?"

He hoped that after she secured her armor of anger back in place she would remember that he'd held her hands, that his kiss had come from the very depths of his longing for her, that he'd bled a little for her, swallowed every desire he'd ever had about her, about Winslow, and hoped that she'd understand he was goading her now for her own preservation.

"That journal doesn't mean anything to you, does it?" she asked coldly. He didn't move. If he turned around, she'd be able to see just how much it meant, how much he despised Winslow for writing it, and himself for seemingly abandoning her to her own terror.

He shrugged. *Oh, Kelsey,* he thought, *if only you knew.*

"It'll make some juicy evidence. That's about it."

"You can really be a bastard, you know that?" she asked.

He shrugged again. "The name doesn't matter. The job does."

She rose without speaking, and left the room without looking at him.

But John could see the rigidity in her shoulders, the stiffness in her spine. Her anger was back in place, she could be tough again. Her guards were up, and her resolve high.

So why did he feel like the bad guy?

Chapter 6

Thursday, November 11
12:45 p.m., Lubbock, Texas

Kelsey hung up the phone, rested her head on the receiver for a moment. The plastic device was hot against her brow. Her ear burned from having been on the phone so long. Was this day never going to end?

John hadn't given her a chance to wallow in the fear the journal sparked in her. Nor had he acknowledged the anger he'd roused just as easily, a fact that, oddly enough, didn't upset her. She found it easier to be around John when angry than when fearful. She only wished anger could override whatever chemistry it was he possessed.

As soon as she'd finally come back downstairs, he'd handed her a list of things to do, including canceling all appointments, all meetings and all support groups. She had started to protest, but a single slow look had stopped her cold. And fanned her resentment even more.

He told her that with each call she made, she was to garner promises of silence, to have whoever she was talking to agree to maintain complete discretion about her, but to call her immediately if anyone were to contact any of her friends or students with questions about her.

He was right to cancel everything, to be so careful. But she didn't have to like it. In fact, she hated it. She was on the run again, even if she was in her own house. She might as well have agreed to the safe house. Except she wouldn't have felt safe there. Here she knew every noise, every single cause of whatever might go bump in the night. Somewhere else, a whole new set of noises, twigs on windows, creaky floors, would have driven her crazy.

Somehow, in her own home, with her things around her, she felt in control. In another house, another place, nervous, scared and out of her element, she would once again have had to trust her entire life and well-being to this one man. And while he wouldn't be a whit less alluring anywhere else, in her own home she knew the place well enough to be able to avoid him at least part of the time.

She sighed and checked the list he'd given her. She had to smile a little bitterly; he had even listed gardeners, as if she had one, let alone a plural. Did he think people on the Witness Protection Program had the kind of money that would allow the hiring of a gardener? She did have a cleaning lady, however, who came in once a week. It seemed a pity she'd have to cancel that, especially with Mr. Tidy in the house; and Tonita would be crushed—she'd probably think she was fired permanently.

It was strange, she thought. Until John showed up, she'd thought of her life as one of being in hiding, constantly on the lookout for danger. She'd followed every bit of advice she gave out to her support groups, her seminar classes.

Then he'd begun his lists of people she should contact, had wire-tapped her phone, arranged people around the house to watch her place, and proceeded to mention the myriad ways her life was easy to trace. There was her Monday grocery trips, her Wednesday dry cleaning pick-ups, the once-every-six-weeks trip to the beautician for a trim, Monday night support-group meetings and all her classes—all of which met at regularly scheduled times. It made her feel she'd been amazingly careless, shockingly open to possible danger.

She made the call to Tonita and sank back into the oak dining chair, glad to feel the wood biting into her shoulders. She was tired, felt drained and was hungry. Chinese food would be good, or a pizza. She wondered if he would object to carry-out. The groceries she'd ordered through his team of observers wouldn't arrive until much later that afternoon.

"I'm finished," she called to the other room. "There's nothing left on my list." She almost added "master" to her statement but decided that even a small gibe would seem a friendly gesture. And they were better off this way, him believing her angry, totally cool, utterly aloof. That way she didn't have to meet his eyes, didn't have to worry about losing herself in his gaze.

Even if it was driving her crazy.

"Did you hear me? I'm all through with the phone."

Almost as though taunting her, the phone rang. She reached for it automatically, and before she could even lift it, John had silently crossed the room and lifted the lid of the little device she'd spilled from his bag earlier. It was now set up on the bar next to the wall phone.

After the screen flashed a series of lights and beeped a couple of times, he nodded at her and pointed to the receiver. He didn't take his eyes from the screen. His concentration alone raised her fears. Could it be Bill on the line? Had he found her so quickly?

She lifted it cautiously, her heart thudding. "Hello?" Did her voice sound as breathless as she thought it did?

"Kel? It's me, Jilly."

John looked as though he might go through the roof. He all but slammed the lid down on his tracing device. "Tell her to get Jenkins on the line."

Kelsey did as he asked and handed the phone over to him.

He listened for several seconds, then snapped, "Hell, I don't care. Tell her she's been blabbing so much the Russians have decided to recruit her as a spy." He listened a second or two. "Tell her the FBI is seriously considering cutting her tongue out as a penalty."

Kelsey had to turn away from him swiftly so he wouldn't see her sudden grin. She bit her lip trying to hold it in. She told herself that John Chandler had three noticeably irritating habits. One, he snuck around like a ghost; two, he could rouse her to almost apoplectic ire; and three, he could make her want to laugh even in a towering rage.

She didn't dare meet John's eyes now. If she did, with her anger gone and her humor alive, she'd be sunk. She'd slip into the depths of that warm gaze and think a million and one thoughts that were totally inappropriate to the situation at hand.

He hung up and without saying anything, went back to whatever he'd been doing in the exercise room. She followed to see what he was up to in there. He was half behind a curtain, fiddling with the locks on her windows.

She frowned. "What are you doing?"

"Setting up alarms," he said around something in his teeth.

"There are bars on the windows," she pointed out.

"Those are decorative bars. They look tough, but a pair of good bolt cutters would snip right through them."

She didn't say anything. She thought of the price she'd paid for those decorative, cuttable bars. After this was all over, if it ended with her intact, she was going after the guy who sold those bars to her.

"How do the alarms work?"

"Anything jars this window frame, or if the glass shatters, it'll set off the alarm."

"They look pretty small. Will they be loud enough?"

"Want to hear one?"

"Yes."

A high-pitched, ear-splitting scream rent the air. It wasn't a woman's scream, but the shriek of a half-dozen fire engines racing toward a five-alarm fire. The sound ceased as abruptly as it began.

"Loud enough?" John asked.

"Yes," she answered coldly. She could still hear the ringing in her ears. "You are undoubtedly the most—"

"Good thing we remembered to cancel your maid. If she'd dusted these windows, it'd probably take us a week to pry her from the ceiling."

Again she had to turn her back on him so he wouldn't see the smile. "Are you rigging every window in the house?"

"Not today. I don't have enough with me. I'll do the downstairs and the side windows upstairs. I'll fill in the rest later."

Kelsey turned back around in time to see him move to another window. When had her anger with him slipped away? She couldn't say. Perhaps it was working with him, or maybe it was while watching him work. He was so very good at what he did. So purposeful, so quietly capable.

She wished suddenly that he could see her giving a seminar or teaching basic self-defense techniques to her students. She was good at what she did, too. Why did she always have to meet up with him when she was running?

She sighed. Was there ever likely to be a reason for being around him other than running?

"Are we going to eat pretty soon?" he asked. Again he sounded as though he was talking around a mouthful of something.

"You sound like you're eating now," she said.

He didn't answer. He started humming the tune of a fast-food commercial instead.

Kelsey smiled, and for the first time since he'd arrived she realized she wasn't frightened, wasn't nervous, wasn't anxious. She was actually standing in the doorway of her exercise room, watching him install minialarms, conscious of feeling relaxed.

This was his doing, she thought. She wanted to tell him she wasn't angry with him any longer, hadn't been for quite a while, in fact. By the time she'd made the first few phone calls, she had reviewed their conversation upstairs and had come to the conclusion that he had incited her anger on purpose.

She didn't want to analyze why he had done it, it was enough to know that he hadn't left her in that box of fear Bill's words had built around her.

Like his little offhand remarks that made her want to laugh out loud, his understanding of her anger amazed and worried her. And made her feel slightly off-balance. It seemed to be saying that he understood *her*. And she wasn't quite sure what that might mean, now or in the long run.

They'd entered a bargain, they had shaken on it. Was he trying to imply that he considered them partners now? That he would really and truly be there for her and expected the same in return?

She'd been looking after herself, all by herself, for so long she wasn't certain she knew how to delegate any of that authority to anyone else. She trained others, gave her support in whatever problem they might be having, but had she relied on anyone other than herself in the past three years?

She realized she hadn't. John was right to ask if she trusted anything, and she'd answered honestly when she'd said not anything or any*one*.

But he'd kissed her, held her hands this morning, hurting *for* her. After the shock had passed, she could recall in minute detail his warming of her numbed hands, the feel of his legs against hers, the crease in his brow, the plea in his eyes.

And she'd seen something she was fairly certain he hadn't even acknowledged. Holding her hands, apologizing for the journal, he hadn't tried to keep the fragile, little Kelsey, he'd deliberately and purposefully cajoled her back into her new self. He may have arrived at her home expecting the former, but he needed the latter, wanted her the way she'd become. Accepted her that way.

"What's for lunch?" he asked, crossing to the last window in the exercise room. He didn't look around at her, only stuffed a few screws into his mouth and immediately set to work on the lock at the window's midpoint.

"Granola," she said. She left the room not bothering to hide the smile this time.

Thursday, November 11
8:30 p.m., Dallas, Texas

Bill stretched his legs to the railing of the balcony outside his tenth-story motel room. The night was cold, but not cold enough to make him want to go back inside. He'd had enough of being inside to last a lifetime. He lit another cigarette and flicked the match over the rail, smiling as the small flame sputtered out in descent.

Kelsey wasn't in Dallas. She wasn't in Fort Worth, either. He'd called every hot line in the books, giving the big sob story about having hurt his wife and needing help from somebody. Counseling, something. And he'd called counseling service centers using his Johnson alias to ask for referrals for a patient of his who needed support-group work. To all of them he'd mentioned hearing of a Kelsey person who he understood was doing some fine work in personal growth development.

He'd even called that twit with the talk show. She wouldn't give him the number of the woman who had called in spilling the beans about Kelsey. If he had time, or if it still bothered him later, he would teach that hostess a thing or two about manners.

But her refusal wouldn't slow him down much.

No Kelsey at this stage? No problem.

That was all right.

He had time, because he was a man who understood the value of that precious commodity. And he had a purpose. A man who fully understood that he never intended to see the inside of a prison again, was a free man indeed. There was nothing he couldn't do.

And he had a handful of names to choose from. Tonight he was a tired salesman who would rather pay cash than even wait for the credit card check. With a weary smile for the benefit of the equally weary desk clerk, he'd signed his name as John Chandler. It seemed fitting somehow.

There had been something between that guy and Kelsey. He had seen it at the trial. It wasn't in the way they had looked at each other, it was in the careful way they *hadn't*. Bill had known. Knew now. He was an expert on human behavior.

He was sure the FBI would have gotten to her by now. But safe houses were only safe from the little well-behaved citizens. Anyone with brains could find them. And he had brains.

He'd underestimated her once, or her boyfriend, Chandler. But he wasn't a desperate man anymore. No. He was free, and he'd find her.

She was here in Texas somewhere. He could feel it. He could almost taste it. He blew out a cloud of smoke, watched it drift on the night air. Soon it mingled with the lights of the city, getting lost in the glow. Kelsey couldn't do the same.

For now maybe, and tomorrow. But soon he'd be circling in, a hawk after the prey that had too long eluded him.

Texas was big, but he was bigger.

And the game was just beginning to get interesting.

Thursday, November 11
8:30 p.m., Lubbock, Texas

John sat in one of the low-slung, exercise-room chairs, watching Kelsey as she worked out. She'd been at it for some twenty minutes and he was the one who was feeling wrung out, and certainly not from overexertion.

He had to tell her about Winslow's possible trail of murders, his possible arrival in Dallas. And had to confess that Winslow had eluded every FBI checkpoint. But how?

He didn't want to be the cause of her face paling, her eyes taking on those shadows that underscored her fear. He was heartily sick of Bill Winslow playing with her emotions, and even sicker over the notion that he could do it all too well himself.

And the truth was, he found her anger easier to deal with than her fear. Her anger made her sharp, clear, responsive. Her fear drove her inside, away from him, away from everyone.

He half smiled, thinking of the day. Kelsey had been cold and unresponsive at best, but she'd done everything he'd asked, from cataloging her friends for him to outlining her routines.

She'd allowed him to take over her life. She'd made every call he'd dictated, and even made him a sandwich for lunch instead of the granola she'd threatened. She'd patiently made out a list of grocery needs and let the FBI shop for her. She hadn't complained when he'd wired her doorways and windows with small alarm devices that triggered upon the slightest touch.

But, thanks to him, she had been as cold as ice all day. And she'd refused a slice of the pizza he'd called in for dinner, fixing herself a bowl of rice instead.

However, after a day in which she poured ice on his every sentence, he found himself wishing he could just tell her the truth, relax in the here and now, forget the danger lurking outside the door, the danger likely to be knocking some-time tomorrow or the next day. But sitting there watching her body gyrate in impossible twists and turns, making his mouth dry with a thirst only she could quench, was driving him crazy.

"Are you ever going to stop being mad at me?" he asked when she lay back on the floor and starting swinging her legs up and over her head. How could she do that?

"I'm...not...mad...at you," she managed to get out in rhythm to her amazing kicks.

"Could have fooled me," he said.

She didn't say anything, but rose to her feet and gave him a swift, hard glance. She dropped her hands to the floor.

"You'd...know...if I...was...mad," she panted, starting to lift first one leg, then the other, pointing her toes at the ceiling.

"I get it," he said. "If you were mad, you'd talk to me, right? You'd join in a conversation, even add a word or two. Right?"

She didn't answer. He thought he saw her lips quirk in a repressive smile, however. There might be hope yet.

She was still angry, but he'd prefer her throwing things at him, verbally sparring with him, to this particular form of torture. He had already checked and double-checked the perimeters of her house. The minialarms he'd installed were on, and the tiki torches out back were blazing away, mak-ing her lawn look like an abandoned garden party. The phones were working, the lights were dimmed, curtains were drawn. How long could she keep moving that way?

He'd even chatted with the team outside via the radio more than once. The second relief team was still in place at their stations, one in back of her high adobe wall, one parked across the street, one probably freezing his butt off while hanging on a telephone pole about a half a block down the street and the fourth holed up in a recreational vehicle in the neighbor's carport.

John would gladly have traded places with any of them at this particular moment. He was pretty sure any of them would have been equally glad to be sitting in this cushy chair watching Kelsey's body in action.

She moved as though each exercise had been choreographed with her fluid body in mind. Hands to the floor, back straight, toes tilted, feet arched like a ballet dancer's, she stretched across the mat, lifting one shapely leg at a time. Her long black hair flipped forward, exposing the gentle curve of her neck, the soft swell of her shoulders.

Torture or not, he didn't move.

"You know what I'd like?" he asked after a few more kicks.

"No...what...?"

"A bowl of that delicious cereal."

She let out a small gasp, then, as if he'd pulled the plug on her, she simply collapsed to the floor. She lay on her stomach, her hands sprawled out to the side. Her entire body shook and a low growling chuckle resonated in the room.

John found himself grinning in a kind of dazed delight. This was a new side to Kelsey, a side he'd never seen before. He'd seen her fearful, tearful, and he'd seen her full of fire. But he didn't think he'd ever seen her laugh, just cut loose and *laugh*. Was that something that came with her new-found identity, her toughness? Did terror stomp out humor?

God, but she was beautiful.

Kelsey lay on the floor, not even trying to conceal her laughter, and even when it subsided, unable to stop her lips from curving into a silly smile. She'd read somewhere that a good laugh burned up as many calories as ten minutes of hard rowing. If that were true, she'd just rowed across the Potomac and back.

She rolled over to her side to look at John. He was sitting in that same chair he'd been in and out of half a dozen times that night. The chair was overlarge, but somehow he made it small. His legs were sprawled out in front of him. Within reaching distance, she thought, although she didn't test this theory. His hands were dangling over the sides of the chair, his knuckles grazing the tiled floor, brushing the fringe of her Oaxacan woven rug.

His eyes were on her. And a gentle smile played on his lips. He'd never looked so approachable, so *ordinary* in an extraordinary sort of way.

"I've never heard you laugh before," he said softly.

"I don't do it very often," she said. Even this reminder couldn't erase the smile from her lips.

"I like it."

She thought about that a moment, then slowly said, "So do I."

They both fell silent, and the moment seemed to freeze in its very warmth. She thought John had never looked so relaxed before and she had never felt so easy in his presence. Was this what sitting around with someone could be like? What that nebulous word "friend" meant? Could there actually be moments when the tension ebbed, the fear receded, and suddenly, for a shimmering split second, a real camaraderie could blossom? She wished she could take this moment and lock it away in her heart, the kind of precious memory to take out on a lonely, rainy day and review with loving care. Would it make her smile later, a smile such as his lifting her spirits, easing the blues away? She thought that just maybe it would.

"I can see I'm going to have to stock up on jokes."

His words implied he'd be seeing a lot of her. More than just a few days of waiting for a sociopath to track her down.

She felt her smile slipping. She shut her mind to whatever it was he was or wasn't implying.

"Charlie's the guy with the lines," John said. He was still looking at her, but Kelsey had the feeling he was seeing other times, other places. She found she was slightly jealous of the half smile on his face, the pleasant memory that claimed him, if only because she'd never seen him look this easy, this accessible before.

Gone was the hard-boiled agent, replaced by a handsome stranger who had a life outside of her recurring nightmare. A stranger who had friends, had been married, divorced and lived places she had only heard about in news stories or through novels. A man who had touched countless lives beyond hers. She felt humbled and a little in awe. She had the odd notion she'd opened a door and was peeking at him without his knowing it.

A sharp pang of longing shot through her. Not the confusing desire she felt for the physical John, but a piercing need to know this relaxed stranger sitting before her now. She didn't want to be just a voyeur on his life, but a participant. The notion scared her and excited her at the same time.

"One-liners?" she asked, just to keep him talking, to cling to this moment, to listen to the altered quality in his voice, the gentled tone, the note of respect tinged with something she'd never thought to hear in John Chandler's speech. Was that because she'd never looked for it before, or was it that he'd never let her glimpse it earlier?

"One time we were staking out this guy. He was a pretty bad character, dabbled in everything from drugs to trapping zebras for black-market sales. Anyway, we ended up in this storage closet, up to our teeth in animal skins, tusks, tails, you name it."

He paused, chuckling at the memory, his eyes on whatever had been in that closet. Kelsey felt her own smile returning, not from what he was saying necessarily, but because his deep rumble was wholly infectious and because he was sharing this memory with her. She propped her head on her hand and leaned there on her elbow, aware of the danger outside her house, and very aware of this moment of peace.

His laughter played on her nerve endings like his touch, making her tingle, making her feel alive. Alive, perhaps, for the first time in three years. Not safe, certainly not secure, and not even necessarily happy even at this moment, but she didn't search for those elusive feelings now, she only lay there on her exercise mat, drinking in the sheer glory of living.

He went on with his story, with whatever Charlie had said, and she even chuckled at the punch line, but she found she wasn't so much listening to what he said as to the things he wasn't. Things like finding humor even in the face of danger, other things like placing one's whole life in another's hands and trusting that life to be cared for. And deeper messages, like living with a restless loneliness and an ache that never quite went away. She could hear these unspoken words, could feel them lingering in his tone, see them in his eyes, on his half-curved lips.

His friends were lucky, she decided.

And she wasn't.

Was that what life came down to, she wondered, simply a matter of being lucky or not? The notion was inexpressibly sad.

"Kelsey . . . ?"

Had he asked her a question? She blinked, realizing she was looking right at him, but as he had done earlier, she'd been seeing other faces, other times, alternate realities.

"Where were you raised, John?" she asked.

"In a little town in western Montana," he answered. Something shifted on his face. He looked as though he'd tasted something slightly bitter.

"It was bad?"

Whatever that taste was, bitterness didn't quite cover it. A muscle jumped in his cheek before he answered. "Bad? No. Just empty."

"Were you an only child?" she persisted, not quite knowing why it seemed important to do so. Maybe because being interested in someone else chased the demons back into the darkness for a moment. Or maybe because she'd just now discovered how much she didn't know him, hadn't tried to know.

He didn't answer for several seconds, long enough that she wondered if he was going to. "I don't know."

The words were too stark not to be a warning of sorts. He'd called his upbringing empty; not even knowing if you had siblings or not was far more than that. It spoke of pain too intense to talk about.

"My parents died when I was twenty," she said, deflecting the confusion she saw in his eyes. "One of the support counselors suggested that was one reason I was so susceptible to a man like Bill."

"Because you needed someone?" he asked.

"That's what the counselor thought."

"I'm not sure I buy that," John said.

"Why not?"

"Because somehow that puts the blame on you. As though if you hadn't been grieving, or if you had been alert, someone like Bill wouldn't ever have gotten his hooks into you. As if it was all your fault for believing his lies. The truth is, he's the liar. He was the one who hit you. He was the one who tried to kill you. It wasn't anything you were going through that brought that down on you."

She hadn't looked at it that way, and studied it now to see how it felt. She read the sincerity in his steady gaze, the certainty in his posture. He believed what he said. For at least two years now she'd been handing out tips cn how to avoid men like Bill Winslow, but was there a way to avoid the con men, the crazies in the world if they really wanted to trap you?

A person could put up guards, take care not to be in situations that invited trouble, but against a hardened criminal mind, what chance did anyone really stand? She sighed in some measure of relief. She felt as if John had handed her some missing jigsaw puzzle piece, one that had been absent for at least thirteen years. The why piece.

There wasn't a real answer to the why, except that in John's puzzle piece, her name wasn't written across the top. He didn't find her at fault for having believed Bill's lies, for having bought into his maelstrom. John's words were an absolution of sorts. And she found that some aspect of her needed to resolve the past.

"Thank you," she said.

"For?"

She smiled a little wistfully and looked down at the bright pattern on the rug. "Oh, for being here, maybe. Or for making me mad this morning. Maybe for kissing me. And for holding my hands before that. For telling me Bill wasn't my fault. I don't know all the reasons."

He didn't say anything and she looked up to find him leaning back with his eyes closed, his face toward the high ceiling. She couldn't read his expression, but her heart seemed to beat more slowly, much harder in her chest.

"I still want to kill him," she said softly.

His eyes opened and he slowly lowered his head to look at her again. "So do I."

"Somebody has to," she said.

John knew this was the time to tell her, no matter how much he might hate it. "Kelsey, two men were killed this morning in West Virginia." Quickly, he told her what they knew about those deaths. "We're afraid Winslow may have been involved."

He steeled himself for the tightening of her features, the pinched look around her eyes.

Her hand, which had been tracing the pattern on her rug, stilled for a second, but she didn't tense up. "You mean you think he killed them. Why?"

"Why do we think so? Or why did he do it?"

Kelsey smiled sadly. "There's no guessing *why* Bill Winslow would do anything. What makes you think he did it?"

"He shook one of the FBI tails in a café in Leesburg, Virginia. The tail saw him getting into a medical supplies salesman's car."

"And the doctor?"

"A stop on the salesman's route."

"God," she said softly, distantly, almost as though they were talking about a complete stranger instead of the man after her. "It's just a matter of random chance, isn't it? You know, I'd always thought it was just me. Just between Bill and me, I mean. But it's not, is it?"

"I doubt if it ever was just that," John said quietly. "He'd conned plenty of other people before he found you. And he'd hurt plenty of others, too. A person doesn't suddenly just become crazy."

"But to kill someone?"

"Maybe he finally went all the way around that bend," he offered.

"Maybe."

"But if he really did murder that salesman and that doctor, you won't have to worry about our killing him or not."

"Why not?"

"Because they'll either lock him up forever or give him the death sentence."

"If he's caught."

"He'll be caught."

"It doesn't make any sense to me," she said.

"What doesn't?"

"He tries to kill me and fails. He gets off in three years for good behavior, even though he's practically drawn a map explaining how he plans to do it again. He goes out and kills a whole bunch more people, and now he's free and I'm basically in prison.''

"You're not in prison," John said.

"No, but I'm surrounded by the FBI—not that I'm complaining about that. It's just that I don't understand his being able to take lives—or even try to take them—and being allowed to live.''

"There's a fairly large controversy in this country over that very issue,'' John said wryly.

Kelsey smiled again, but without bitterness. "Do you know that before Bill hired someone to kill me, I was one of the strongest advocates for penal leniency?''

"They say that for every mugging, a hard-liner is born.''

"Is that what I am, a hard-liner?''

John smiled and leaned his head back again. "I'm not going to tell you what I think you are.''

"Why not?''

His head came back down, his gaze slammed into hers, and the look in his eyes stole her very breath. "Because I'm on duty, because for all you don't want to admit it, you're still scared. And because next week, next month, I'll be on assignment somewhere else.''

"Well, that puts me in my place, doesn't it?'' she said easily enough, despite the sudden tightness in her throat, the hurt at his words and the understanding of what he *wasn't* saying. He'd been angry at himself for kissing her three years ago. And for doing it again this morning.

"Do you know that you're the first person I've kissed in three years?'' she asked, almost dreamily.

He did that stillness trick of his, seeming to freeze in place.

"And it was you I kissed three years ago.''

"Kelsey...''

"That makes it more important than it warrants, don't you think?'' she asked.

"No," he said. He slowly leaned forward, propping his elbows on his knees, his brown eyes never wavering from hers. "No, I don't think it's unimportant, Kelsey. I never did."

"I was too scared to ask you what you meant when you said 'It shouldn't have happened.' Right after we kissed, I mean. Do you remember that?"

His smile was completely gone now, and she felt vaguely guilty about having made it go away. A frown had replaced it, but it wasn't a frown of anger, even of discomfort.

"I remember," he said. "You shouldn't have been scared to ask. I meant that I should never have kissed you. I was married, I was assigned to protect you. You were too vulnerable, too raw for me to..."

"I was," she said, not needing for him to continue. "I was too vulnerable. Am I now?"

"Are you asking me to kiss you again?"

"I don't know. Would you if I did?"

"Is that a trick question?"

Kelsey chuckled again and without even thinking about it held out her hand. She didn't stop to analyze it, she just did it. Her heart was pounding uncomfortably now, and yet she felt oddly at peace.

He stared at her outstretched palm for a long while. She didn't pull it back, she left it in the air between them, more than a gesture, less than a command. It was an invitation in the purest sense of the word, and it was a plea.

"Kelsey..."

When she didn't say anything, didn't move in any way, he sighed heavily. He slid from the chair in a wholly fluid motion, standing over her one moment, kneeling beside her the next.

"I'll say it again, if you won't take it wrong," he said. "This shouldn't be happening." His warm hand wrapped around hers. He held it for a moment, just staring at it as if he'd never held her hand before, as if he'd never seen it before, either.

He lifted his eyes and met hers squarely. He repeated his statement, as if by repetition he could convince himself to get to his feet. "This shouldn't be happening."

"I know," she said, and all too sadly, she did know. "But just tonight, just now, can we pretend that it should?"

Chapter 7

Everything in John seemed to be clamoring for his attention, for his sanity. But how could a man be sane with Kelsey lying beneath him, beside him, lids half-closed, lips parted, dark hair spilling out around her like a black aura, having just asked him for tonight, for now? Other men might be able to, he thought, crazy men, or men who had never seen her, touched her, but not he.

He sat down on the floor beside her, not leaning forward, not giving in to the desires raging in him, the need fueling him. But he kept her hand in his. He felt as if he were standing on the edge of a high precipice, the entire future stretched out in front of him and not a hint of a bridge in sight.

"I'm not exactly sure what I meant by that," she said slowly. *Oh, you know all right,* some part of her admitted. She just wasn't sure what she wanted from him, what she expected of herself. She knew she responded to him more than she ever had anyone, three years ago and now.

"I'm not exactly sure, either," he said. She thought his voice sounded sad rather than confused.

"You're not going to, are you?" she asked.

"No," he said, wondering if he'd gone out of his mind. Knowing he must have done so.

"Why?"

Now there was a good question, he thought. Because I'll end up hurting you, he wanted to tell her, and you'll end up hoping someone breaks my heart someday. Because something tells me, it will mean too much, take too much away.

But he didn't say anything, somehow knew he didn't have to, for he could see that knowledge already in her eyes. She'd been hurt so badly, so thoroughly, he doubted if she'd ever be able to believe in someone again, really believe in them, trust them, rely on them.

And he knew, then, that it wasn't just himself he had wanted to run from all those years ago, desperately wanted to run from now. She made him want to do everything in his power, everything humanly and inhumanly possible to gain her trust. He wanted to erase her past, eradicate the shadows from her eyes, the ghosts that haunted her. He wanted to do all of that, and was afraid if he so much as tried, he'd be caught, trapped forever in the need for her, the want of her, and that somehow, in some very real way, he'd be the one left behind.

"Kelsey..."

"It's okay, John," she whispered. "I think I finally understand. It's not enough just to chase away the fear for a few hours, is it? There's so much more involved than that."

How right she was. Was that what she wanted from him? An interlude, something to chase away the terrors that stalked her? Somehow he felt this wasn't the case, but still he didn't feel he understood the true reason for this sudden drop of her fierce guard.

He wanted to tell her all he was thinking and more. He wished he could just shut his mind off. He wished he could just blurt out the raw, unvarnished truth, tell her what he was really like, what he was capable of, and most of all, what he was *not.*

If I manage to save you from this trouble you're in, I'll have to go, I'll want *to go.* He wanted to tell her this, too, wanted her to understand. *I always want to go.* Except once, for a moment, three years ago.

But even then he'd gone.

With her invitation, her question, her hand resting in his, he found he wanted to warn her, to give her truth to use as a shield if she chose. But again, he suspected she could see this as well.

. . . But couldn't we pretend we should?

Her words echoed in his mind, in his loins. And worst of all, he thought, in his heart.

"You shouldn't have to pretend," he said. "Not with me, not with anyone."

"You shouldn't, either," she said.

Wasn't that the whole trouble, he thought a little wildly, that he was more than half afraid he wouldn't be pretending, that he couldn't dissemble with her?

Her hand, tucked in his, trembled, but her eyes didn't waver from his, wouldn't shy away. He almost wished they would. He felt too exposed, too open to her. And that was dangerous.

"I feel like I'm just beginning to know you," she said, smiling somewhat wistfully. "The real you, not just the agent who always dashes in for the rescue."

He returned her smile rather sadly. Did she feel as nervous, as bleak about the future?

"I feel the same way," he said.

After studying him for a few moments, she smiled, rather shyly he thought, and said, "I think I could really like you, John."

He felt as though she had reached deep inside him and laid her soft, delicate hand on some forgotten part of his heart, some door locked so long ago that even his subconscious mind had lost its memory.

Part of him felt the pain of that touching, a primal cry for freedom. Another, the part that never forgot what opening that door could mean, wanted him to fling her hand away, rise and leave her now, leave before she managed to find the ancient lock, touched it with her magic and flung the door wide.

She'd told him, and he believed her, that she'd kissed a man only twice in three years. He was that man. And he'd gently, perhaps foolishly, turned her down when she'd asked him to do it again. To do more, perhaps.

With anyone else, it would be so easy to take her into his arms, feel her soft, firm body against his, revel in the scent of her, the taste and feel, but with anyone else he wouldn't feel he was diving into dark waters, waters that might not ever allow him to surface again.

As if reading his conflicting desires, his inner struggle for right and wrong, his fear of her, his overwhelming need for her, she lifted her free hand and laid it on his arm. Had she done more, stroked his face, touched his thigh, he might have had the strength, even the cowardliness necessary to pull away from her.

But she simply rested her hand on his forearm, as if she understood, as if she were reassuring him, telling him not to worry.

He had thought her fragile, had seen her afraid and had thought her vulnerability signified her weakened state. He'd been so wrong, he realized now, staring at her, seeing in her wise eyes all the strengths he hadn't understood before.

Vulnerability wasn't weakness, wasn't fear, he realized now. It was a certain candidness, a guileless honesty that lingered in a quiet hand, a still body, an unwavering pair of blue, blue eyes.

And he understood her. She hadn't been offering him a night as a means of avoiding the fear, of keeping the danger at bay. She'd been giving him that glimpse of the real Kelsey, the complete woman without the trappings of toughness, without the wall of fears, the impenetrable barrier of hurts.

The sheer magnitude of her gift unnerved him.

And sobered him.

Kelsey felt his regard the way a plant drinks in sustenance from the sun's rays. His eyes said so much more than he would ever allow to pass his lips, she thought.

If he touched her now, she would melt. She knew that, and conflictingly, both hoped he would and prayed he wouldn't. She responded to him too much, too thoroughly. And she was letting him see the real Kelsey tonight, and was reveling in that showing.

She felt she was ending all the lies she'd been living for the past three years, maybe even the past thirteen. Somehow in laughing with him, in lying on this floor, his hand holding hers, her free hand upon his arm, just resting there, nothing more, she was cleansing her soul of the terror, purging it of the string of half-truths, the endless array of white lies. She felt wholly and totally free.

That very freedom made her think of how vulnerable she could be without her ever-present anger, both in actual terms and because it made her remember her long-ago self, that Kelsey who was dead and buried. How much she would have liked to have known John before she'd met Bill. How much she would have enjoyed his easy humor, his struggle with tact, his protectiveness.

And how very much that enjoyment had come along at the wrong time in her life.

Now, more than ever, she needed to be the warrior Kelsey, the woman who backed down to no one, and not just because Bill Winslow was once again after her life. She needed that strong part of her to remain on the surface because she was altogether too susceptible to this man holding her hand. Whenever he was around she was too conscious of his gaze, his touch. He couldn't move without her being aware of his body, his warm brown eyes, the long supple fingers of his hands, the rather quirky smile he displayed on occasion.

She turned into a veritable marshmallow whenever he walked into the room. And that she didn't need. She would be crazy to lean on someone else, to rely on them. She would be crazy to give in, even for a single glorious minute, to the way he made her feel. She didn't dare trust anyone.

He slowly lifted her hand to his lips, pressing a soft, warm kiss against her knuckles. She felt that touch echo through every pore of her body. She should pull her hand back. She'd already said too much, invited too much.

But she didn't withdraw her fingers, couldn't somehow.

She reminded herself that she didn't dare trust anyone. Not even the long arm of this very capable representative of the law. She knew that, she felt the truth of it, but with his lips against her knuckles, his eyes on hers, that truth seemed distant and oh, so far away. In the case of John Chandler, how could she possibly help giving some measure of trust?

As if he'd been traveling along the same mental lines she had, he lowered her hand to his lap, and said, "When I was a kid, I used to think that grown-ups had all the answers. Like magic. Poof, they turned a certain age and suddenly all this incredible knowledge just poured into their heads."

Kelsey smiled. She felt so lazy, so *at peace*. Was there something wrong in accepting this brief moment of respite?

"And then, I *was* older." He chuckled, though the sound was slightly bitter. "And I didn't feel any smarter, no 'poof' for me. For a long time, I thought that maybe, because I was raised in the orphanage, I didn't get the same information everybody else got. Do you know what I'm saying?"

She nodded, though she wasn't sure she did. He was an orphan? That was why he didn't know about other siblings?

"But now I think we all just stumble around, trying to act like adults, wondering how we got here, when did we stop being kids and have to start paying rent? Do we ever get to stop for a minute and be a kid again?" He asked the question as though he really wanted an answer, expected her to be able to give him one.

She felt as if he'd touched a nerve. She'd left everything she knew or loved behind. She'd been slipped out of one life and into another. And she'd worked hard to build this one, to safeguard it. But where were the little joys, the laughter, the simple thrill that children seemed to possess to such abundance that they could actually ride that roller coaster of life with all its fears, its brilliant peaks, its despair-filled valleys, get off and immediately want to ride again?

She wanted to tell him that they could, they could signal the great pitchman in the sky and hop on that joyride and soar to the clouds, forgetting routines, mortgage payments and ex-husbands who thrived on the thirst for murder.

But, unlike John, she had been one of those unlucky few that did acquire the full knowledge of adulthood in one fell blow. Three years ago she'd started that new life, an abjectly adult life. A life based on guardedness, on single-minded adherence to regimen, to rebuilding strength.

She shook her head, more saddened than she could let him know. "There's no going back," she said.

"And there's no tomorrow," he answered.

"Why?"

He just looked at her for a long while, then said softly, "Because tomorrow takes a commitment of some kind, don't you think?"

She wasn't sure. She was only just beginning to feel a fringe touch of the future. "For someone in survival mode," she said finally, "tomorrow is just a word."

"Because there aren't any guarantees?" he asked.

"There aren't any guarantees about anything. Why should tomorrow be any different?" she queried.

He set her hand down, laying it against her chest, careful not to brush his fingertips against her breast, too careful for her to be unaware of his studied caution. In an odd way she felt she had let him down somehow, rebuffed him, though if she had, it was only with the truth.

"I want to be friends," she said suddenly, feeling as if she blurted it out. Her desire for friendship was truer than he might ever know.

He hesitated and she wanted to retreat, but she didn't look away. God knows what strength enabled her to meet his eyes directly, unwaveringly.

"What do you mean, *friends?*" he asked.

And in his asking she understood. They were not so different, she and John. They were cut from the same mold, perhaps at alternate times of their lives, but both had been harshly cut, roughly hewn. They were the product of too little love at times when they needed it, too much punishment when they didn't deserve it at all.

She drew a slow, deep breath. This was too important to let slide in a glib phrase or an offhand remark. But she also sensed, and really felt, that a modicum of humor couldn't hurt. "You know, *friends,* that seven-letter word meaning pals, buddies, cohorts in crime."

What on earth was she doing? he wondered. The last thing he wanted to be was her *friend*. An image of a "big brother" came to mind. An uncle. Worse, a eunuch. He'd kissed her for God's sake. After that, no man would settle for just being her *friend*. Still, given the circumstances, it would certainly be easier to be around her with that tag on their uneasy relationship.

She went on. "Friends tell each other secrets. They exchange hopes and dreams. And . . . I think friends are there for the good times, not just the bad. Not just the rainy-day times, but the moments that are so great, so wonderful that you have to have someone to share that with you."

She felt as if she'd simply trailed off, although she'd said everything she had to say. He looked at her as if she was a peculiar pattern that had just erupted on her Oaxacan rug.

"I don't have many high times," he said roughly. Almost accusatorially, as if she'd changed the rules on him somehow.

"Neither do I," she said.

"But when you do..." he said slowly, gropingly "...you want to share them?"

"Don't you?" she asked. "Don't you want to throw everything to the wind once in a while and simply laugh until you drop?"

"What are you asking me to do?" he asked. His voice was harsh. Nearly angry.

"I'm not asking you to *do* anything. All I want to know is that if I ask you to come over on Saturday night for a pizza and a pitcher of beer...or champagne and caviar on Thursday, that you'll say 'what's the occasion?' and you'll try to be there."

"I live in D.C., Kelsey."

And that was the ultimate leveler. "Yes," she said, looking for the exception to the inevitable rule. "But you have a telephone."

"But I'm not home all that often."

"I have the feeling you're dodging the question," she said, and her heart felt close to breaking. She'd never wanted anything as much as what she was asking now. *Let me in. Open up that heart of yours, the one that sees the humor in a closet filled with zebra tails and elephant feet, and allow me to laugh, too, allow me a chance to see you.*

Just let me believe that all this will be finished, that everything will turn out all right, she wanted to beg. Don't you get it, Chandler? What I'm asking for here is a glimmer that there will be a tomorrow, a day after the cataclysm, a morning after the confrontation. I'm asking you to pretend that there will be a future, that tomorrow you and I don't really see.

"Do you know that you're the only person, besides my case worker, who even knows my real name?" she asked.

"You want to be friends?" he asked, overriding her thoughts. His question was harsh, she thought, and, half-ironically, *unfriendly*.

She smiled, she couldn't help it. "Well, not if you don't want to."

"In my world," he said, "friends stand at your back, cover you, and then make damned sure your front side's covered, too."

"You're luckier in your friendships," she said. "My back has always been exposed."

"Except once," he said, and shifted his gaze to the carpet.

"That didn't last long, did it?" she asked, and immediately regretted the question, for it sounded bitter, angry. She truly hadn't intended it that way.

"No, I guess from your perspective, it didn't," he said. "Not exactly friends by your definition."

"So, maybe my back is still exposed," she said.

"It's against the floor."

"That's a terrible place for a back," she shot back.

"Better than up against a wall."

"Where do you think Bill is now?" she asked. The question sounded like a non sequitur. But it wasn't. Not really.

"I would imagine he's holing up somewhere in Middle America. Ohio. Indiana. One of the smaller airports, someplace we haven't placed a trace detail."

"What do you think his chances of being able to get through are?"

His lips pursed, and Kelsey was glad he wasn't looking directly at her; he'd see too much want in her eyes, he'd be able to see just how vulnerable she really was. He could make the fears go away, he could rid her of this gnawing anxiety. He could, but he hadn't. Wouldn't.

"I think he'll probably get through," he said. "Not because we aren't smart enough or strong enough to take him first, but because he's focused. He's driven."

She didn't say anything, merely considered his analysis. He was right, there weren't any odds to be leveled on Bill Winslow's ability to get through. He would find her. If not now, then later.

The phone rang and John's casualness disappeared so abruptly she had to wonder how much of him had really been sitting there with her and how much was still working on the case, thinking of all the angles, the difficulties. He whipped into the other room, had the trace device operating and was lifting the receiver before she'd even pushed to her feet.

"Hello?" she heard him ask as she crossed the room. She felt slightly unsteady, as if she'd been drinking or had overexerted herself.

His back was to her, and she found herself wishing the phone hadn't rung, that the night had remained inviolate, that the cares of the world had faded for a brief span of time. She wanted to go to him, to lean against him, to feel his warm, broad back beneath her palms, to press her cheek to that wide expanse.

But those thoughts were reminiscent of the old Kelsey, the woman who needed someone, who had relied on others to do what she should have been capable of doing for herself. Why did that other Kelsey, that scared, pitiful Kelsey seem less lonely? Why did that alternate, former self seem more fortunate than she?

"Fine," he said. "Just keep the rotation random. If he does show up, we don't want him witnessing the changing of the guard."

She realized, as if for the first time, that John was truly doing his job. It wasn't just a matter of baby-sitting Kelsey for a few days, he was attempting to take care of every possible contingency, right down to arranging the outside teams changing shifts at seeming random. All for her protection. All for her safety.

Had she been so busy trying to prove to him that she was capable, tough and able to handle her own life, that she'd made his job more difficult?

"Hell, yes, it would have been easier at the safe house. But there was no arguing with her. We're here now, and I want everything as smooth as glass."

She had her answer. She had made it more difficult. She tried telling herself that her safety was more likely here, with a confrontation now, than if she slipped away somewhere and hoped for the best, wished that the future would resolve itself. But hearing the regret in his tone made her waver.

"Right. Okay, call me first thing. Good." He hung up, disconnected the tracer and turned back around. He did that stillness thing when he saw her standing in the doorway. His gaze sharpened, sparked by a hunger Kelsey suspected was largely unconscious.

Whatever the myriad reasons he might have had for refusing her earlier, it hadn't stemmed from any lack of desire. She thought of the way he'd sounded on the phone, wholly connected, utterly in tune with his assignment, and suspected that was the primary reason for his seeming withdrawal. He couldn't love her with one ear tuned to the door, to the outside. And he was on assignment.

He wasn't a man of half measures. She'd seen it in his eyes, he was all or nothing at all. And yet, she remembered, it had been he who had reminded her that nothing was either black-or-white, that too many shades of gray lingered in between.

With that flicker of hunger in his eyes, his body rigid with the strain of staying across the room from her, she thought that a shade of gray must be what she was to him, a nebulous, unanswerable shade of gray.

"I'm going to bed," she said softly. She didn't ask him to join her, though she wanted to, ached to have his warm arms surround her, would have killed to have him kiss the darkness away, the fears into oblivion.

"I'll get the lights," he said casually, although his expression was far from easy.

Her heart pounded uncertainly as she mounted the stairs. She felt his gaze follow her around the curve, could feel his stillness even after she passed out of sight and made her way down the short hallway to her bedroom.

She peeled out of her exercise suit and tossed it into the hamper. As she showered, trying to let the water soothe her jangled nerve endings, she tried understanding her own brazenness that evening. She couldn't deceive herself into believing it had been born from a need to hide from the fear that raged inside her. And she couldn't hide behind the notion that he had so thoroughly defused her anger that passion had immediately swept in to fill that void.

No, she had offered herself, had asked him for himself, out of a nearly raw honesty. A true desire for him. A desire so intense, so achingly abandoned that her request had slipped from her without thought, without rational consideration.

She toweled off, trying to determine whether or not she was embarrassed by his refusal, by her request. That she wasn't was entirely of his making. He'd offered her something equally precious in return—his friendship. Of the two, his might have been the more valuable, since it was the more difficult to realize.

She slipped on a blue satin negligee and pulled the band from her hair, shaking it free. It was hot in the room, steamy from the shower, made hotter by her thoughts about John. She moved to the window and slid her hand beneath the curtain to undo the catch.

All hell broke loose.

John had long since finished turning out the downstairs lights, rechecking the window and door locks. He was in his room, already having shucked his shoes, socks and belt. His shirt was unbuttoned and he was just shrugging it off when he heard the unmistakable scream of one of the window alarms.

He had his pistol in hand and was out the door and into the hallway in less than a mere second. He didn't stop to determine where the sound was coming from. One thought dominated all. *Kelsey.*

He covered the hallway in a single leap and threw open the door to her room. He followed his outstretched gun into the room, his eyes raking the perimeters.

He frowned in puzzlement and in a measure of heart-stopping fear. Kelsey was standing beside the window, her hands over her mouth as though holding in the scream that still rent the air. She was unharmed. No one was holding her at gunpoint, no one was half in or out the window behind her. Yet the alarm continued to shriek.

"What the hell—?" he yelled over the cacophony.

Her hands dropped from her mouth. Her eyes lit in relief and she stepped forward a pace. "I didn't mean to," she said, a child's instinctive excuse leaving her lips.

"What?"

He lowered his weapon, crossing the room swiftly and raising a hand to the window alarm. He tripped the switch and the noise ceased as abruptly as it had begun. His ears still rang with the horrible scream. His heart was still pounding with the intensity of his fear for her, his gut-wrenching certainty that Bill Winslow had somehow breached the security of her home.

"Why the hell didn't you just turn it off?" he barked at her.

"Because you never told me how," she snapped back.

"Any *child* could've figured it out!"

"You're so busy being Mr. Macho, that you don't fill me in on things. I didn't even know you'd put those damn things in my window!"

His temper, fueled by his fear, exacerbated by his frustrated desire for her and his recognition that she was correct in at least one of her accusations—he hadn't told her how to turn the bloody things off—made him see red.

"You want in on everything? Fine. There are alarms on every damned window in this place. And they're hair-trigger. And you turn them off by pushing the little white button at the back. You turn on the tracer device by lifting the bloody lid and waiting for the green light. The teams outside are shifting on quarter hour, in consecutive sequence. There's an FBI operative posted at every major airport. Every police department in Texas has been issued a photograph of Winslow and an all-points has been posted for him. Your dippy friend has eaten dinner and made a pass at Hendricks, and I'm damned sick of you taking your anger over your ex-husband out on me!"

He hadn't realized that he'd been advancing on her as he delivered his diatribe. He didn't know it until he saw her start of surprise as her legs made contact with the bed behind her. But she stood her ground, he thought with some admiration. As usual, she wasn't going to let him see her afraid.

Seeing her that way, her chin raised, her lovely body encased in blue satin that matched her eyes, her hair a cascading black cloud around her shoulders, his anger evaporated. He raised his free hand to his forehead and rubbed it, trying to get a handle on what it was he had to really be angry about.

Himself, he thought. For turning her down, for wanting her so much he could taste it, for backing her across the room like some crazed lunatic, for reacting to that alarm not as a seasoned agent, but as a man.

"I think it's probably a medical fact that you can't rub a frown out of existence," she said.

He smiled slightly, dropped his hand. He couldn't look at her, couldn't let her see what he'd only just now realized himself. He stared instead at the large, Southwestern painting over her bed. It was starkly beautiful in a harsh way. And lonely somehow. And strong. And it seemed, in the soft glow of the bedside lamp, to epitomize Kelsey herself.

His gaze dropped to the bedside table, took in her .38 lying there at the ready, a cold nighttime partner at best. He crossed to the telephone and lifted the receiver. Without looking at her, he punched in the number of the primary relief outside.

"Chandler. It's okay. I tripped the window on accident." He wasn't sure why he felt the need to say it was his fault, and he didn't particularly want to analyze it. It was more an apology to Kelsey for yelling at her than any real covering up of a goof.

He replaced the receiver and spoke, without turning to meet her eyes. "I'm sorry," he said, realizing he wasn't identifying what he was apologizing for exactly.

"I'm sorry I set off the alarm," she answered, a slight quaver in her voice.

He looked at her then. To his amazement, the quaver hadn't been produced by tears, by a reaction to his anger. She was biting back a smile, literally holding it in with her teeth.

"Why you little . . ." he said, crossing the final distance between them and taking her arm. It was a mistake. He shouldn't have touched her. Because now he wasn't sure he'd be able to stop.

Slowly she released her hold on her lower lip. Her mouth parted, moist and all too inviting. Her eyes were wide and bluer than copper-burned flame. And she stood perfectly still.

He felt the entire universe was waiting, on hold somehow. Something deep inside him seemed to break, a shattering so thorough, so complete, that all the dams in the world wouldn't be able to contain what was released.

"I can't pretend, Kelsey," he said hoarsely. His voice seemed to come directly from that ancient door inside him, was perhaps, the screech of the lock turning itself.

"Neither can I," she said slowly. "Not about this."

With the very real feeling he was making the single biggest mistake of his life, and at the same time knowing that this was one mistake worth risking life for, he lowered his lips to hers.

Chapter 8

Kelsey closed her eyes, feeling his warm lips brush hers, tremble against her own. Butterfly soft and as light, his mouth skimmed across her sensitive lips, her cheek and lower, to the pulse throbbing near her collarbone.

She shivered as the light kiss seemed to radiate out in rippling spirals, making her arms and legs tingle, kindling a fire inside her. She had witnessed the war waging in him, watched it on his face, in his eyes, felt it in the delicate brush of his lips.

And she'd heard the truth, a raw, pained veracity in his voice when he told her he couldn't pretend, but didn't know whether his words foretold his winning or losing that war he'd fought. But in his slightly shaking body, his almost incorporeal touch, she felt the sharp, poignant empathy that sprang of recognizing the depth of his honesty with her, of hers with him.

That this cost him, she knew now. She suspected it might just well be as much as it was costing her.

She felt she understood so much more about him after tonight, from his laugh, from his painful inner struggle, from finally seeing him as something other than her knight in slightly tarnished armor.

He, too, was running from something. Not her, perhaps, but something. She'd heard it in his anger, had seen it in the dazed way he came back to himself, studied her room, looked at her.

He, too, had been wounded in some essential way, at some crucial time in his life. And like her, he needed a measure of peace, of friendship, a respite from the storms in his life, a chance to share the candlelight before the nightmare resumed.

She returned his light kiss, not arching to him for more, not asking or demanding anything other than this soft, almost sweet touch.

When that thought changed, when the tenor of their kiss altered, she couldn't have said. She only knew that he wanted her as much as she wanted him, that it was no longer a matter of there being too little between them, but now, possibly, too much.

She clung to him as he pressed more deeply, reveling in his weight, craving more, aching for him to touch her, for the touch of him. She wondered at her abandoned thinking, her complete disregard for tomorrows or maybes....

She felt the cold touch of his gun barrel against her thigh and shivered. It was a grim reminder of the reason he was in her house, the reason why he'd burst through the door. And it represented everything she'd worked to become and to overcome.

As if reading her mind, he stepped away from her and set the gun down on her dresser. He dislodged the bullet from the chamber and loosened the clip. But he did this without taking his eyes from her. She felt he was still kissing her though he was some five feet away.

He wasn't turning her down now. And she had the very real feeling that there was no turning back. She felt this moment had been destined, perhaps three years earlier, perhaps a lifetime ago. They had been meant to come together, to meet, to grapple with conflicting emotions until the essential, inexorable quality that drew them became the most important element.

As it was now.

His gun discarded, he slowly came back to her. He stopped inches from her, not touching, not speaking, just drinking her in. She could feel the want emanating from him, a palpable force, so strong it was nearly visible. And she knew he could feel it being matched, taken and sent back in identical strength, parallel intensity.

Tonight, this minute, she felt they were total equals, both afraid, and both risking the lowering of their all-essential guards.

She didn't wait for him to come that last step forward. Instinctively she knew she had to meet him halfway. She stepped into him, her arms lifting to his shoulders, her hands lightly grasping the back of his neck. For a moment he hesitated, then with a surety born of extreme need, his hands encircled her waist and brought her roughly to him.

Yes, she thought. They were both equal now, both breathing raggedly, hearts thundering against each other. Here, in the safety of each other's embrace, for this time, they could drop the barriers, forget them, because tonight, now, they were more than the knight and his damsel in distress. They were a man and woman who were also friends.

She shivered as his lips found the sensitive spot behind her earlobe and she arched to meet his trembling hand. And she knew suddenly and with complete surety, that later they would neither one be the same. How they would be changed, in what ways, she couldn't begin to guess, but the changes would take place nonetheless.

She should have listened to him, she thought; this *shouldn't* be happening.

He lifted a hand to her face, cupped it, and pulled away to look at her.

"Ah . . . Kelsey."

He said her name like a prayer, or a promise. And at his tone, tears stung her eyes. She wanted to say something to him, something that would create a bridge between this moment and tomorrow, but there was nothing to say, no words that could create something out of thin air, could make something happen that wasn't meant to be.

"I've never wanted anyone as much as I want you," he said.

The raw honesty in his voice, in his words made her feel a little afraid, more than a little nervous, but she met his eyes without hesitation and what she saw there allayed her fears, stole the tension from her limbs.

His gaze burned with hunger, and yet a nearly staccato pulse throbbed in his jaw, telling of his own vulnerability, his own need for control of his desires, his fear of hurting her, his fear of her hurting him.

Her eyes seemed to grow heavier, her body pliable and languid. And she moved now, raising her own hand to his cheek where that muscle thrummed. "Yes, John," she said, as though he had asked a question.

Achingly slowly, he bent over her again, stretching his legs forward to meet hers, holding her tightly against him, letting her know the extent of his want, his need. Kissing her fully now, he exhorted her response, elicited her insanity. Letting her taste him, as well, he raised his hands to her face to hold her steady, to keep her with him. She could have gone nowhere else, would never want to again.

One of his hands slipped behind her head, into her hair, pulling her even closer to him as his other slowly roamed the curve of her shoulder, followed the line of her arm, the swell of her breast. Slowly, as though she were a cat and he was soothing her, waiting for her to purr, he stroked her waist, her hips, her waist again, and the side of her breast.

She'd laughed tonight, she'd felt like crying at the different expressions on his face and she'd felt alive. But now, with his lips against hers, his rock-hard body pressing against her, she understood she'd only guessed the half of it. *This* ... this communion of two people, this was being alive.

Now, tonight, like emerging from a chrysalis, an entirely new self was winging its way to the very meaning of life, a self that had always been there, just never called forth before. She felt totally and wholly there, absolutely connected with the moment, with the man, with her own heart.

As if sensing her dawning awareness, he pulled up again, drawing in air like a drowning man, stilling his touch, opening his eyes to meet hers. She raised her hand to his chest and felt his heart thundering against her fingertips. He mimicked her action and she knew he, too, could feel her heart pressing against his warm palm.

And suddenly she didn't know what to do, didn't know how to continue. She trembled with want, with need, but couldn't voice it, didn't dare to.

He pulled away from her slightly and she wanted to cry out at the abandonment, but didn't. In a contemplation as slow as his touch had been, he studied her face, probed her thoughts. In the most frightening lowering of her guard, she allowed him to see at will, to understand whatever it was he was searching for.

He had to close his eyes against the sheer intensity of what he could see in hers. She'd stood there so bravely, he thought, her face slightly upturned, her chin squared, her shoulders back. She looked like a dark Valkyrie at the gates of Valhalla. He knew she was giving him all she thought she had to give. And selfishly, he wanted more.

He wanted from her what he himself couldn't give. He knew she was open to him, was giving him this measure of trust, a quantum leap across the barriers she kept locked into place around her.

But he also knew that, like him, she was wrestling with the need to hold on to that fierce guard, the need for perpetual distance.

He wanted to reassure her, to offer whatever it would take to make her feel she could trust him, could let herself go. But there were no words that could convey that promise, because words weren't enough. It had to come from total faith.

A faith he couldn't offer her in return, a faith he didn't believe he had to offer at all. But trust or faith or even simple hope didn't matter now. Because she was standing before him now, a satin touch away, and his resistance was gone, as absent as the sun at midnight, the moon on a summer's morn.

He'd fought this internal battle earlier, had told himself he'd won. But he hadn't. He'd lost the moment Charlie called him in Washington to let him know he would be seeing Kelsey again. He'd lost it the first moment he'd glimpsed her dark silhouette, and he might as well have tossed in the gauntlet when he'd kissed her this morning, for the war had truly ended there.

He had only been dodging the inevitable, stalling the admission that he wanted her more than thought, needed her more than he needed breath.

He wanted her trust, yes, but knew he had yet to earn it. Wasn't sure he would receive it even then. And most of all, was certain he would not be able to return it in kind. But now, tonight, he had the rest of her, and she him. Tonight they needn't be alone.

Slowly he unclenched his hands and let them hang loosely at his sides. He had argued with himself long enough. He had fought to do the right thing, to walk away from her, leave her in her room, lock himself in for the night. *Before*

*it was too late for either of them. Before it was too late for
him.*

But he couldn't. Because walking away from her wasn't
the right thing. There was nothing *right* about it.

He lifted his eyes and met her liquid blue gaze. There was
a hint of tears in her eyes where slow passion had burned
only moments before. He held out his hand and whispered
her name. His voice had gone with his sanity, and he'd never
needed anything in his life as much as he needed her to understand that he couldn't walk away from her now, couldn't
call a halt.

Slowly she placed her hand in his and allowed him to draw
her forward. He didn't pull her into his arms, nor did he release her, but continued to hold her hand. In a peculiar way,
he felt they were making up for some long-ago lost time. It
felt as if they were simply courting. It was an old-fashioned
notion, and yet vaguely poignant. He was standing in her
bedroom, at arm's length, merely holding her soft hand in
his.

A tear clung to her cheek and slowly etched its way down.
His heart wrenched at the sight and he lifted a finger to
catch it. It felt solid against his skin, and seemed a concrete
manifestation of his choices.

"Don't cry, Kelsey," he said. His voice was harsh, as
though he hadn't spoken in years. "I don't want you hurt."

"You won't hurt me," she said softly, changing his
words, altering their meaning. And he knew it wasn't true
and hated himself for knowing it.

He drew her into his arms then, as much to shield her
from this truth as to hide from it himself. And as her body
grazed his, he found he couldn't think. She felt so good
against him, fitting him, molded to him as though she'd
been carved from the opposite side of the same clay as he.
He held her tightly, aching for her, striving to put a permanent end to the distance between them.

He ran his hands over her back, down her sides, up the soft curve of her neck. He lifted her thick, silken hair and tested its weight in his hands, let it spill from his fingers, tease her shoulders, cloud around her face. It covered her, him, like a warm fluffed curtain, releasing her scent into the air. He held a strand of that soft black to his nostrils, rubbed it against his face and felt he was drowning in a sea of senses. He ran his fingers through her hair, against her scalp, smiling as she groaned, sighing when her knees buckled against his.

He caught her to him and swiftly lifted her into his arms, catching her beneath her knees. Her arms slid around his neck as a small gasp of surprise escaped her lips. He bent his head and kissed her smile.

He should have felt foolish, he thought. But he didn't. He'd never felt this good. Not once in his whole life.

Feeling as though he could climb mountains, scale brick walls without need of ropes or ladders, he held her tightly against his chest, turned slowly around in a large circle, loving the way she held her head back, letting her long black hair trail behind her, beneath her, truly a cloud now, riding on the wind.

He may have spoken to her, she may even have replied, but when he thought about it later, all he remembered was how perfect she felt in his arms, how right he felt holding her.

Carrying her this way, having lifted her from her feet in her own bedroom was symbolic somehow, the warrior image, the conqueror, the bridegroom. But it was more than that, it was a sign of respect, of honor, perhaps even of pure animal desire to display strength before the chosen partner.

The glow from the hallway cast a pool of soft gold on the floor of her bedroom and as he stepped into it he felt an almost preternatural recognition of the light, as if it symbolized some kind of oblique blessing. And the soft radiance from her bedside lamp glimmered across the satiny bedspread, making the large bed look like a dark pool of glistening water.

Gently, almost reluctantly, he laid her down upon the bed, then stretched out beside her and took her into his arms, more than half-afraid that he was taking her into his heart, as well.

She moaned, a pleasured, pleading exhortation, and he couldn't have denied her, himself, what she wanted, what he craved.

He ran his hands along her satin nightgown, not caring nor understanding how it fastened, but aware it was as silky to the touch as her skin, that he could feel everything about her beneath it.

Kelsey shivered anew as his hands roamed her body like an explorer might a new terrain, eager to discover each hitherto unknown valley or mountain, desperate to capture it all. His hands were firm and masterful, knowledgeable even in mystery.

His lips captured hers, not lightly now, not in friendship, but in demand, in hot, harsh want. His body pressed against hers, letting her know how she aroused him and she half rolled into him, slipping her leg around his, aching for closer contact.

He tasted of the pizza she'd given him for dinner, the iced tea he'd drunk with it. He tasted like autumn, like walks in the woods. And he moved against her with the surety of autumn clouds moving across a near-winter sky, with purpose, heavy with need.

He neither hurried nor seemed slow in his deliberate ministrations. His hands cupped her face, played in her hair, dipped beneath the scooped neckline of her negligee to the aching breasts beneath it, searing her with his touch. His fingertips snared a taut nipple and played it between pad and fingernail, so gently, so lightly, she felt his hand a magnet and her body unalloyed iron. She arched sharply to him and he applied greater pressure, greater urgency with his lips, with his fingertips. She bit her lower lip to withhold the groan of longing he induced.

He shifted his mouth, his heated tongue, from her throat, lower, lazily trailing a blaze across her collarbone to the rounded scallop of her negligee. With his tongue he traced the contact point of the satin's edge with her skin, making her shiver, making her want to writhe. He raised his hands to her shoulders and slowly slid the straps from her arms. Raising her slightly, pulling the negligee down, he followed its removal with his lips, kissing her shoulders, her collarbone, her breasts, first one, then the other.

He rolled her over him, sliding the soft material from her as he did so. His fingers lingered against her hips, gently explored her rounded buttocks, her satin legs. She moaned at his touch, at the promise in his lips, and wantonly kicked away the negligee.

She reached for his shoulders, and, in her eagerness, her feeling of drowning in sensation, fumbled with the already unbuttoned cotton, struggling to free him, desperate for the feel of his skin against hers. Finally, she accomplished her task and, raising above him, arching her back sharply, she threw open the sides of his shirt, tugging the last of his tails from his trousers. She slid her hands around him and pulled him to her, herself down to him.

His skin was hot against hers, and she could feel his heartbeat pounding against her aching breasts. His lips recaptured hers, his tongue beating a rapid message, a code of some kind, a promise. His hands roamed her body more rapidly now, as though he were memorizing the texture of her skin, the curves and flares.

In a fluid motion, he again rolled her over, this time beneath him. Dipping his head, he nipped at her breasts, lightly, playfully, then with assiduous attention. He pulled back slightly, exposing her bare body to his hungry gaze.

He watched as he touched her, watched her reactions, then, as though his hands belonged to someone else, watched his fingers as they circled her turgid nipples, taking them and pulling softly, shaping and reshaping. He replaced his fingers with his mouth, his tongue. When she arched upward, he pushed her back against the bed, still teasing her nipples, laving the sensitive underside of her breasts. Straddling her knees, he cupped the shape of her breasts, molding his hands to her form, stroking her, caressing, imploring. He slipped his hands behind her, beneath her, and kneaded gently, then with greater purpose. She couldn't have withheld the moan that escaped her.

Sliding from the end of the bed, he trailed his hands down her legs, massaging her, letting his hands say far more than words could ever have supplied.

"My God," he said as he stood. "There isn't a woman in the world as beautiful as you are, Kelsey."

Languorous in his regard, liquefied from his hands, his mouth, she could only stare up at him, taking in his bared chest, his throbbing body. He shrugged and his shirt fell to the floor. His hands moved to the fastening of his pants and she found her mouth was dry in sharp anticipation.

His pants dropped to the floor to join his shirt and he stepped free of the constrictive undergarment. Her breath caught.

He had called her beautiful; he was a Greek statue come to life, all muscles, curves and angles. He bent over his clothing and pulled something free. She heard the rip of the foil wrapper and was grateful for the sound, the consideration. One touch from him, and all practical considerations had flown from her mind.

"Thank you," she said shakily. "I would have forgotten."

"I almost did, too," he said huskily. "Hell, you make me forget my own name."

She heard the rubbery rustle, caught a slight whiff of the plastic odor and shivered again. This was real, this was happening. The thought made her insides coil tighter, her anticipation build another notch.

"It's John," she murmured.

"Ah-h-h. Then you must be Kelsey."

Somehow the light banter took on greater meaning than either might have intended. It sounded almost algebraic—if A, then B...if it was John, then it could only be Kelsey. The notion warmed her, made her smile.

"Oh, yes," she said, reaching up for him.

She expected him to again stretch out beside her, but he didn't. He crawled onto the bed over her, facing her, planting his knees beside her feet. She felt him touch her calves, her knees, and moaned as his hands again met her body.

With his nails, he brushed the crisp, curly hair at the apex of her thighs. "You're still blond, here," he said.

Her smile broadened, but she didn't say anything.

"I like knowing secrets," he said, his voice husky, his breath hot against his discovery.

At his first touch, she jumped, unused to such a riot of sensation, such a beautiful fire that he created in her, unfamiliar with the sheer wanton pleasure his fingers, his tongue, produced.

Her body arched to meet him, her legs involuntarily opening to grant him greater purchase. He touched her as though he were a sculptor and she the willing body of clay. He stroked and shifted, molded and moved, plied and teased her until she felt she was nothing more than a stunning creation of pure molten fire.

"Please," she murmured, her fingers pulling at him, begging him.

The raw note of appeal in her voice nearly undid him. There was so much he wanted to give her, so much he ached to have her feel, and so little time. Just one night, one blessed night. For tomorrow would bring regrets, confusion, and, in all probability, one very real Winslow. And then he'd be gone. One way or another, John would be gone.

So tonight, right now, he had to complete every fantasy, every dream either one of them had ever harbored. Her closed eyes, her hands now clutching the satin bedspread as though she needed grounding, her inchoate pleas, all conspired to make him hurry this moment, rush the exquisite pleasure inherent in her body, in her unconscious trust. But he couldn't do that to her, wouldn't do it to himself.

She'd been hurt before, and tonight, tonight was his chance to erase those memories, not forever, but for now. Tonight was his opportunity to supplant the pain with pleasure, to override the fear with ecstasy. And to seize every pleasured sigh, each writhing motion for himself.

"Oh...John," she whispered, and he had to fight the urge to raise his head, to bury himself in her warmth, her liquid longing. Her fingers tugged at his hair, pulling more sharply now, and he could feel her legs quivering, her muscles tightening and he pressed on, refusing to abandon her there, to leave her stranded on that plane of incompletion.

He moaned in answer to her short, ragged breaths. He felt he would die at any moment. Her taste was honeyed and her feel liquid satin. Her legs arced outward, trembling, quivering. And still he wouldn't stop. He slid his fingers deeper, kneaded her buttocks, kissed away tomorrow, kissed the past farewell.

Then he felt her convulse around him, arching off the bed, a swift bucking and her muscles pulled at him sharply, strongly.

And his resistance eroded, his control shattered.

She felt she had been consumed by the fire he started in her, and flung to the far ends of the earth, neither in this body, nor away from it, but somewhere in between. She opened her eyes and saw him rise above her, his eyes ablaze with want, with need.

His hands scooped her up, yanking her limp form to him, holding her tightly, fiercely. His elbows braced them both and with a harsh, raw groan, he slid into her, making her cry out, not in pain but in intense relief. They moaned simultaneously, and equally in tune, began to sway. Slowly, achingly slowly, they moved apart, then together, seeking that perfection she knew instinctively they could share.

She ran her hands down his back, across his buttocks, and felt his fingers tighten on her shoulders. She raised her legs and locked her ankles over his thighs. He made some sound, a ragged, dissonant sound of supplication, and pressed deeper, and deeper still.

His breathing snagged, then resumed, rougher now, and as ragged as his voice had been. He moved swifter, faster. Deeper, harder, taking her with him, growling something, a thousand promises, as he rocked.

She clung to him, pulled him tightly against her, needing to feel his full weight against her, wanting it, craving it. He drove harder, faster yet, and she pressed sharply against his rigid buttocks, calling his name out loud.

As if this were a trigger, he arched upward suddenly, convulsed, and ground out her name through clenched teeth, clamped jaw. His body violently shook, and hers did, as well. She felt him shaking her inside and out, calling for her, begging her to stay with him, to follow him.

The fury, the explosiveness of his release sparked another of her own and she held him, clung to him desperately as she again scattered into a million glassy shards, needing to stay with him so that she wouldn't be lost in whatever world he'd taken her to, so that she could find her way back home. Home with him.

And she felt him there, in the multicolored universe he'd spun them to, the dazzling, dizzying rainbow lights that surrounded them both, nurtured them, caressed them as they finished the most primeval of waltzes.

All too soon the shaking, thrusting dance was ended, the lights dimmed and the mystical music wound to a halt. But he didn't move from her, and she held him tightly to her, cradling him, soothing him as gently as he'd stroked her earlier.

She had never felt more in tune with anyone in her entire life, thought she never would again. It was as if, in their exchange, they had melded more than bodies, more than the need in either of them. It was as if their very souls had conjoined, had blended, fusing together in a single, wholly precious moment of unity.

It wasn't until his breathing had slowed to a deep, regular pattern, until his heartbeat had steadied to a soft, rhythmic thudding, that she loosened her fierce-gentle hold on him.

"I wish tonight would never end," she murmured against his cheek, against the roughness of his after-five shadow.

He stiffened slightly, then relaxed again. "The night is young," he said, stroking her hair, pressing his lips to her shoulder.

The night was young, he'd said, and he was right. The hours stretched before them like jewels on an unguarded beach. But she'd caught the nuance in his stiffening, in his cautious words. Tonight *would* end.

And tomorrow, with its uncertainty, its lack of definition, would dawn all too soon.

Chapter 9

Friday, November 12
8:05 a.m., Dallas, Texas

Bill flipped open the thick Houston Yellow Pages the maid had secured for him. He tipped her five dollars. He might need her again.

He looked up Women's Services first, then, at the cross-reference, turned back to the counseling section and grimaced at the number of referral services listed. But he knew that diligence paid off. It always did.

He hauled the phone from the end table to a comfortable place on the bed. He leaned back against the pillows and punched out the first number.

He introduced himself as John Chandler with the FBI. He smiled.

He struck pay dirt on the fifteenth call.

All in all, he thought, it helped to know the right people.

Friday, November 12
8:30 a.m., Lubbock, Texas

* * *

John stood in the shower far longer than was necessary. He let the water play over his slightly aching muscles, his stiff back, his weary head. He lathered himself and watched as the suds sluiced down the drain trailed by warm, clear water. If only illusions could be as easily rinsed away.

Everything about the night before stood out in his mind. The touch of her, the feel of her velvet skin against his, her honeyed scent and warm hands. And, dear God, her total and wholly unconscious trust in him.

He had wanted that trust, had craved it. Drew it out and buried himself in it again and again and again. And what he'd feared most had happened. She'd reached inside him and snapped the lock on a door he'd always made certain stayed sealed.

He was a different man this morning. A different person. The John Chandler of the past was just that—the past. He felt stripped of his defenses, shorn of his guards.

What in the name of all that was holy was he going to do now?

This wasn't an assignment anymore. It was a pledge. And she wasn't a case, she was a part of him. How could he possibly remain objective—not, he admitted wryly, that he'd been anything resembling objective from the very beginning when it came to Kelsey—when protecting her was no longer a matter of hope, a matter of skill, but one of absolute necessity?

He'd never felt so frightened of anything in his entire life.

Friday, November 12
8:45 a.m., Lubbock, Texas

Kelsey absently fixed breakfast, bacon and eggs, toast, even fried hash browns. Her mind was on the sound of the shower, on the man inside it.

He had taken her places the night before that she'd never dreamed of seeing, shown her the priceless treasures of his touch, his heart.

And this morning she was afraid of him.

Not afraid he would hurt her, per se, but afraid of the intimacy they'd created the night before. It seemed too isolated an intimacy, too intense a meeting. They had shared every nuance of what a union could be, could mean. They had tasted every drop of paradise and then had had to wake up to reality.

She was certain he'd seen that reality in her wary, confused gaze, in her swiftly averted face. She'd felt it in his slow, almost apologetic touch as she rose from the tousled bed.

And she'd known that she'd hurt him somehow, when he left her bedroom, going to his own room and a separate shower. She'd felt he was taking the sun with him as he left, for all the warmth he'd created the night before went with him. And all the trust.

The reality was unjust, she thought angrily, because it spelled out too many things she wished were simply left nebulous, forgotten in the wake of their loving through the night. But the reality was clear: John was on assignment; she was just a case. She resented a hero; he reveled in being one. And the day was bright, too sunny, and she was only a shell of the woman he'd helped her find the night before.

Dear God, what was she going to do? How could she face him now, no guards, no defenses, and worse, with no fears? How could she be tough when she felt so weak, so soft?

The phone rang and she turned the burners off before turning to answer it. At the last second she remembered John's tracing device, the instructions he'd yelled at her after she'd tripped the alarm. She smiled slightly, flipped the tracer's plastic lid open and waited for the classic green light before lifting the phone receiver.

"Hello?"

"Is this Kelsey Dobson?" a male voice asked. He sounded choked with emotion. She could empathize. She was too. At least he seemed able to voice his.

"Who is this, please?" she counterquestioned from long habit, and with John's explicit instructions in mind. But she felt no fear. She watched the little tracer device blipping and heard its computerlike hum. She would have to ask John how far-reaching it was, if it was hooked into a larger machine somewhere, a broader complex.

The man on the phone gave a short, bitten-off sob. "I hit my wife. I don't know what to do. I think . . . I think I need help. A friend gave me your name. Said you might be able to talk to me. Or talk to her. Said you know about these things." Another sob followed his pathetic tale.

Kelsey felt her stomach tighten, her heart soften. The man sounded in terrible pain over what he'd done. It wasn't rare for a man to feel horrible about hitting his wife, but it was fairly uncommon for the husband to be the one seeking the help.

For this reason alone, Kelsey resolved to do all she could for him.

"I'm sorry," she said. "I know how much pain you must be feeling. And your wife, too."

"Oh, God," he moaned. "You don't have any idea."

Kelsey caught a glimpse of John coming down the stairs and forced herself to turn and face him. She was sorry she had, for she felt her reaction to him to her very core.

His hair was freshly combed, his shirt crisp and buttoned. Socks and shoes covered his feet. He looked ready for anything, and totally closed to her at the same time. He raised his eyebrows in question, but looked as though he were vastly relieved to have business to attend to, not to have to face her without some kind of task between them.

She shook her head, but wasn't sure what she was telling him with the negative. That the person on the phone had nothing to do with his "case"? Or was it deeper than that, something to do with the harsh reality of day when contrasted with the soft shadows of last night?

The tracer device beeped as the small machine let them know the origin of the call had been located.

"Hello?" the voice in her ear quavered. "Are you there? Can you do something?"

"I'm afraid I don't normally handle things like you're talking about, Mr. . . . ?"

"I need some *help!*" the man burst out. "Please, lady. I need help right now."

"I can give you the names of several very qualified—"

"No."

Kelsey felt a sharp chill work through her at the single, muted negative. She nearly dropped the telephone in sudden, skin-crawling revulsion. She *knew* that voice. She knew it as intimately and thoroughly as she knew her own voice, had known John's the night before.

Bill Winslow.

She had heard him use just that muted tone before lifting his hand to her, had heard that same implacable note before he'd stripped her and made her beg for mercy. She'd heard it during his trial when the defense attorney had asked him if he had intentionally hired someone to kill his wife.

"No," he'd said then. And he'd sounded just as uncompromising.

She felt a gut-wrenching fear gnaw through her icy veins and the fear was fueled by the realization that he knew who she was. He'd found her assumed identity.

Bill knows my name, she thought wildly. If he knew that, he knew more, *he knew where she was.*

She turned to John in unspoken supplication.

She didn't know what expression rested on her features, but it must have spelled out her sudden anxiety with crystal clarity for it galvanized John into swift action. He waved a hand at her to keep talking and slowly picked up the small receiver on the tracer device and held it to his ear before depressing the listening switch. He nodded to her.

Her hand shook as she again placed the receiver to her ear. She felt she might be sick, but with John's hand beckoning her to continue, she said with scarcely a noticeable tremor in her voice, "I'm sorry, sir, I—I don't think I can help you."

"But you have all the answers. I've been told you know everything."

"S-sir—"

"Don't be so modest. You can't fool me." A low, rasping laugh, the kind he'd always emitted just before testing some new heinous punishment, seemed to waft evilly from the telephone.

Kelsey bit her lip to keep from crying out. And at the same time, clamped them firmly to withhold the too long, pent-up rage she wanted to unleash upon him. She wanted to scream at him, to yell every invective ever created, to rip him with the sharp edge of language.

"Tsk-tsk, Kelsey," he murmured. "You never could do anything right."

"Damn you!" she yelled, and hurled the receiver from her, sending it flying to the end of its bouncy, curly cord. It seemed to dangle in midair, like a cartoon image, then jounce back at her, striking the bar instead in a deafening clatter. She ducked, reflexively, and then stared at it as though it were a physical connection to Bill, as though his voice had turned it into a snake and it might bite her.

John swiftly retrieved it and lifted it to his ear. "He's gone," he said, not looking at her, not even really aware of her, she thought, watching as he dropped it back onto the wall base. He yanked it back up almost immediately, apparently heard the dial tone he wanted, then without setting the tracer receiver down, punched in a string of numbers.

"Our boy's just checked in...no, I don't know how he got the number. I didn't get a chance to ask him," he said dryly. "Here's the coordinates the tracer logged." He read off two different sets of numbers.

"Yeah, as soon as you can. Yesterday would be good. Now, look, we're going to want two more teams, circles of eight blocks... Twenty-four hours... Make it three days. Right. Call as soon as you hear." He listened for a moment, then all but exploded into the phone, "He's *what?*"

Kelsey stepped back a pace at the harsh overtone of shock and fear that rippled through those two words. Was she reading him right? John was scared? If John was feeling fear then something was terribly, terribly wrong.

"Damn it, get those teams in here, *now.*"

He replaced both sets of receivers and slowly closed the lid on the tracer device. He stood for a moment with his back to her, his hands resting palms down on the bar. Finally he turned around.

"Okay, that's it. He knows where you are. He'll be on his way."

Kelsey felt as if she might faint. It had been one thing to argue with John about staying there when Bill Winslow was in Virginia. It had been fairly easy to argue that she felt safer in her own home than elsewhere when Bill was out there somewhere not knowing her new identity, not aware of her life in Lubbock. It had all been easy because it was the truth.

But now it seemed an entirely different matter altogether after actually hearing his voice again, knowing he'd found her, knowing he was really coming after her. It made all her talk of preparation, professionalism, even anger, sound like the braggadocio of a second-grader on the first day of school. *I ain't a-scared of him. I can punch his lights out any day.*

Any day was here, and she didn't think she'd be able to walk to the kitchen without help, let alone take on her ex-husband. Especially now that he'd graduated from socio to psychopath. She drew a deep, steadying breath.

She knew what she had to do. She knew how to do it. The time had come; that was the only real difference. The long, long wait was finally going to be over.

"Why did you say, 'he's what?'" she asked. It seemed to be the only rational thought in her head.

John frowned heavily. "Our investigators found his fingerprints all over the medical supplies salesman's car. And in the doctor's office. West Virginia's pushing for extradition."

It was a perfectly logical explanation, she thought, but she knew it wasn't what had made him pale, wasn't what had made him stand with his back to her, shoulders rigid with shock.

"If he's caught," she said. Should she push him on the question? Would it be like the night before, no then yes?

"When. *When* we nail him, he'll be going up on murder one."

"You're trying to say we don't have to kill him now, is that it?" she asked. Her fear was steadily receding. Was it because he no longer looked frightened, or was it deeper than that? Was it because she had the feeling he was protecting her from something and she resented it?

John frowned sharply. "No, that's not what I'm saying at all, Kelsey. What I'm trying to tell you is that we can go to a safe house now. It's not just a matter of an ex-husband with a bad case of sour grapes. He's a killer, a rabid dog. And now he'll be locked up forever."

"But he's out there now, free." Tell me, she begged silently, unwilling to voice the command-plea aloud.

"He won't be free for long. He's leaving too wide a trail."

"He's in Texas now. He's killed two, probably more, people." She saw his eyes flicker, read some unspoken emotion in the swift, hot gaze. "He doesn't have anything to lose," she said honestly, callously.

"Exactly. Which is why I'm reneging on our bargain. We're getting you out of here and to a safe house. Right now. This minute."

"No," she said again. But she wanted to ask him why, why now? Why after last night, after the past two days? What had he heard during that phone call that made such a tough FBI agent like John Chandler so afraid he wasn't thinking straight?

She could see he wasn't going to tell her.

Instead he said, "Look. He is undoubtedly on his way here already. We've got people at the airports, the bus stations, but we had people at the airports two days ago, and he still got in."

"Leaving a trail of dead bodies behind," she offered in a falsely reasonable tone.

He snapped at her. "Precisely why I'm not leaving you here to be number four."

"Number four?"

"They matched his prints in the beauty shop, too."

Kelsey was silent. "Did she dye his hair first?"

"Damn it, Kelsey! What the hell difference does that make? He killed her. After—" He bit off whatever he was about to say. He needn't have bothered, she thought. She knew Bill.

"Was that what made you go pale?" she asked.

He nodded once, sharply, and then turned his head aside. His mouth was set in a fierce, grim line. His hands were clenched deeply in his pockets.

She didn't want to know any more. Didn't need to know the details, didn't want to hear whatever horror Bill had done to make John look sick.

In an odd sort of way she felt somewhat vindicated. Certainly she wasn't relieved that anyone else was terrorized by Bill Winslow. And to give him his due, John had always believed her about her husband's capabilities. But that parole board, those idiots who had smilingly signed his release, the judge who had issued a concurrent sentence, thereby shortening what should have been life into a capsulized three years, all of those people would have to sleep with what they had done, not just to her now, but to three other families, as well.

God, how she hated the justice system for it. Hated Bill for it. Was even mad at John for not understanding her wholly justified anger. She must have made some sound of disgust for he shot her a hard look.

"There's only one body I don't want left behind now," he said.

She smiled coolly. "That makes two of us," she said.

He smiled back, but she could see that he was far from easy, a Grand Canyon away from relaxed. The smile didn't even come close to touching his eyes. She felt as if she might be looking in a mirror at a male version of herself. The thought unnerved her a little.

He ground out, "So you see, we still have time to get to a safe house."

"No," she repeated. She went back into the kitchen. She dished out a plate of the cooling eggs, bacon and hash browns. She had forgotten toast. He could have cereal, she thought wryly. She almost said as much aloud, but didn't think he'd appreciate the humor at the moment.

"Kelsey..."

"Give it up, John. We both know Bill." It was odd to think of a man capable of killing so many people as even possessing a first name. Someone who was able to kill— murder—three people, try to kill a fourth, shouldn't have such simple humanity as that denoted by a first name, a nickname at that.

She went on. "He's on the run, he's obviously ruthless. He's managed to avoid every man the FBI had in place to stop him. *What's going to stop him in Lubbock?*"

"Me," he said.

''Not if you're playing nursemaid in some safe house. We've been over and over this. Don't you see? Let's say he gets here and is watching my place after you've gotten me away. It won't take him long to figure out I wasn't here. He knows me. I may have changed, but no one changes that much. He was married to me for ten years. He probably knows my small habits better than I do.''

What had she said to spark a spasm of pain across John's face, to make him look as though she'd struck him? The fact that she'd been married to Bill for ten years? He knew that. That Bill knew her habits? He would have to know them. Just as she knew his, which, she thought, was a singular ace up her skintight sleeve.

''Kelsey—''

She interrupted whatever he'd been about to say.

''And your 'team' might never even see him. Probably won't, because that's how he operates. He was only tried for conspiracy to commit murder, you know, not all the million little schemes and scams he had running. He's smooth, and he's good. So, he'll get here and see your team, and then he'll go into hiding. And wait.'' She slammed the plate of still cooling food down on the countertop. The plate didn't break, though she couldn't have said why not.

''Are you through?'' he asked.

''No. No, I'm not. The program hides me, changes my name, my life. Bill waited three years, writing horrible things in that damned journal of his. He gets out and in less than three days has already found me again,'' she said. She marched across the kitchen, planting her hands against the bar separating them. ''And you and I both know that it would only be a matter of time before he finds me again.''

''If it hadn't been for that damned jiggy-headed friend of yours—''

''He would still have found me, John. And you know it. Jilly made it faster, sure. But that's all she did. He would have discovered some other means, some other way. That's how he is. *Relentless.*''

He didn't say anything and she pressed on. "He's *after* me. He's got nothing to lose now. He'll just keep coming.''

"He's killed too many times, now,'' John said. He looked mad enough to come over the counter at her. And sad enough to simply turn away. He looked as though he had expected the change in her the night before to be absolute, to have eradicated every vengeful thought she ever had. Well, she thought harshly, what she felt wasn't vengeance, but the need for pure and simple survival.

"He'll never walk the streets again.''

"No. That's not going to cut it. He didn't kill those people because of some vendetta with them, he probably wasn't even *angry*. They just represented an obstacle to him, an obstacle to getting to *me.*'' She held on to the bar as if it were the only constant in a world gone crazy.

She went on angrily, desperately. "That's all I was to him three years ago. Something in his *way!* Now, if he comes here and can't find me, he'll wait again. And when you're gone, when your team isn't there anymore, even if I've gone back into hiding, have a different name, a different town, another new life, he's going to find me.''

A racking sob nearly choked her and she had to close her eyes before continuing. "But, then, you wouldn't be there.'' The words were out of her mouth before she'd thought them through, before she'd given them any kind of consideration. They seemed to hang on the air like the lingering scent of coffee, the smells of the bacon and eggs, more real somehow than she would have guessed they could be.

He rounded the bar and took hold of her shoulders, shaking her slightly. She hadn't even realized that she'd been all but screaming at him, hadn't known tears were streaming down her face. But they weren't tears of pain, tears of fear. They were tears of anger, of the need to endure.

"Okay, Kelsey. Okay.''

"I want it finished, John. One way or another. I don't even care which outcome it is. Don't you see? It just has to be *over*. It has to be *over*."

John didn't want to argue with her. Couldn't. She was right. It did have to be over. It had to be finalized once and for all. And he was going to see that it was.

Kelsey's angry, tear-streaked face, her defiance, her analysis of the situation, had nearly torn him apart. He pulled her roughly into his arms, held her fiercely to him. "You're right, Kelsey. Oh, honey, you're right. We won't go anywhere, we'll stay here. We'll get him." He stroked her hair with his hand, pressed her face against his chest. He could feel her tears, hot and damp, felt her shaking shoulders, her trembling body.

And he vowed she would never cry over Winslow again. Never be afraid of him again. Never, ever, have to face the future with Winslow dogging her. *I promise you this, Kelsey,* he thought, but couldn't say the words aloud because they needed a concluding phrase . . . something he couldn't give her, something like, I promise because I'll be there for you, in the *future*.

"If we don't finish it now, today, tomorrow, then sometime very very soon," she said, her voice muffled against his chest. "Nights like last night are just m-moments, just s-something to lock away like a photograph or a scrapbook. I can't live like that, John. I need more than that."

She wasn't talking about just the need for resolution with Bill Winslow. He knew she meant far more than that, even if she wasn't aware of it.

He didn't know what to say to her, didn't know what he was really feeling. Shocked, irrevocably altered, scared, even numb. And mad as hell at Bill Winslow. And himself for not knowing how to match her honesty, not having the words to tell her what the night had meant to him, that he recognized what she had done to and for him. That it had been far more than one-sided.

But as usual, the pretty phrases wouldn't come, couldn't make their way from his heart to his mouth.

"Do you always have this much trouble with your cases?" she asked, laying it on the line, her voice almost childlike in her earnest need to know.

"No, Kelsey," he said immediately. He gave the ghost of a chuckle. "You're anything but a routine assignment." He *still* couldn't give her the words, a phrase that would promise a tomorrow, the simple words that would turn things around, make everything okay. He was the doctor who patched the wound, but withheld the prognosis of hope.

But, strangely—and somehow hurting him, though he didn't know why—those he said seemed to be enough for Kelsey. Her hands circled his waist and clung tightly. The humor she'd shown him the night before bounced back. "Well, that's good to know. I'd hate to be routine," she said, and gave a slightly watery chuckle.

He wondered if he imagined her lips had pressed, for the merest heart-stopping second, against his chest.

"I'm all better now," she said, and pulled away.

He thought, she's lying. She was far from okay and his words were far from all she needed to hear, deserved to hear.

He sighed heavily. He wasn't the man to tell her.

But he wished to hell he was.

Kelsey swallowed. It was less a matter of moistening her throat than keeping down a host of half-baked ideas, unformed questions. But had he read them in her eyes? Could he read them in her touch, in his? He'd read her without hesitation the night before, had known everything, anything, about her without question. Why were there so many unanswered queries now?

"It'll be all right, Kelsey," John said heavily, sighing a little as he spoke. He sounded tired, not sleepy, but bone weary, filled with the kind of ennui that assails overworked FBI agents on assignments that have gone awry.

His tone rankled, it conjured too many contrasting emotions from those he'd inspired the night before. Only *hours* before, she corrected herself. He couldn't know it would be all right. *No one* could know. And no one should make promises they couldn't guarantee.

Least of all John Chandler whose very touch was a promise in and of itself.

"I'm sorry for falling apart," she said stiffly, turning away from him.

"Don't apologize for that," he said, letting her go. Too easily, she thought, really hurting now.

"Was there something else I should be apologizing for?" she asked sharply, meeting his gaze with a stringent, go-to-hell look and then turning her back on him. She could see from his shocked expression that she'd hit the mark, though she didn't have the slightest clue what he thought she should be apologizing for. Wanting him? Trusting him?

"No," he said, but the quick, rough rub of his jawline said otherwise.

"There's too much between us now for cat and mouse," she said.

"And there's not near enough to warrant you lashing out at me like this," he responded tersely.

She felt as if he'd slapped her. He was right, she shouldn't have verbally taken a hit at him. Her only excuse was that it was backlash from Bill Winslow, from the years of learning to mask her feelings by hiding behind others. But when he negated last night, when he said there wasn't near enough between them...she felt she wanted to curl up, shrivel away.

That couldn't be true. Could it?

"Kelsey..."

Again she tried hiding. "It doesn't matter, anyway, does it?" she asked.

He paused for what seemed like minutes. Then he sighed harshly—angrily?—and finally said, "Kelsey...we don't have time to philosophize about this."

"You're right," she said, not agreeing with him in the slightest, but accepting the inevitable. "We don't."

She started to leave the room.

"Kelsey."

She didn't turn around to look at him, she only stopped at the base of the broad stairs and waited.

"I hate that this is happening now. I didn't know what to say to you this morning. But I didn't mean to duck out of it this way. Are you listening to me?"

"Yes," she said. She half wished he hadn't added this, hadn't so swiftly cut to that proverbial chase, hadn't so immediately defused her anger, her hurt, with his honesty. As long as she could hate him for belittling what had passed between them the night before, she would be safe.

Without that anger, she would be forced to truly acknowledge the events of the morning, the feelings he roused in her. Even though she'd resented him reverting to the professional agent, she would have welcomed hating him for being insensitive, could have whipped her anger to a fever pitch and used it to survive the next few minutes, hours, days.

But he had brought the night into the day and was now waiting for an answer. This was the agent, and he was also the man who had loved her more tenderly, more thoroughly than anyone had ever done. He deserved more than her childish anger, her fear-guided temper.

"I'm listening," she said.

"What happened last night . . ."

She didn't turn around when he trailed off, but she did smile crookedly. "If you say it shouldn't have happened, I'll open fire on you."

She heard the merest breath of a chuckle.

"I won't, then," he said, effectively saying it, anyway.

"Good," she said, thinking it was anything but that. "Because then I'd have to tell you those bacon and eggs on the stove weren't for you."

"I'll put them in the microwave," he said.

"You eat. I'm going upstairs for a little while," she said. Stop me, she begged silently. Hold me.

He paused, then said slowly, disappointing her, "Listen. This is for real now. Stay away from all windows. Even if you hear something outside, don't go near a window. And, if you love me, lock your bedroom door anytime you go in there. And don't open it for anyone but me. Got that?"

She felt as though his words were an odd sort of epitaph to their union that had lasted only one night, one silken blanket of hours, a hiatus in a storm she didn't even understand. *If you love me,* he'd said. But the phrase had been offhand.

Or had it?

"No one but you," she said softly but very pointedly.

She mounted the stairs without asking the most obvious question of all, a question that only occurred to her now with horrible implication. What if you aren't there to be the one knocking on the door?

John watched her stiff form climbing the stairs, feeling as if the best part of him were leaving with her. Who but Kelsey could have come up with a semihumorous line in the face of such incredible danger?

He'd seen the look on her face at her recognition of the voice on the telephone. She had been mind-shatteringly terrified, her lovely face drained of color, her lips suddenly dry and pale, her eyes wide with confusion and abject horror.

And suddenly whatever hatred, whatever disgust, he'd felt for Bill Winslow before escalated. That this man could do this to Kelsey, when only hours before John had seen her skin dewy with passion, her eyelids languorous, his name upon her lips, made him actively *hate* Bill Winslow.

He didn't want to fan her anger, he'd discovered a different passion in her now. He'd diffused that fury and turned the hunger, the need, elsewhere. But what she needed from him at this moment, what she craved most from him, he couldn't give. She needed a new future, a real future. And he was a man who lived in today only, from one assignment to another, never pondering the vague, uncertain tomorrow.

Kelsey was one woman in a million. In a hundred million. If ever there was a woman to make him catch a glimpse of a future, it was her. But, in an odd way, she was like him; she also wasn't living for tomorrow, for a future. She was living for a single moment in time, a confrontation. A shootout at the Not Okay corral. Winslow or her. John sighed. He knew all Kelsey wanted. He knew it because he knew himself too well and understood that confrontations and futures don't mix.

But somehow, this morning, he couldn't seem to think straight. Too few hours of sleep, too many memories of Kelsey in his arms. Whatever the cause, this morning all he could seem to understand clearly was that Kelsey might very well be that one woman to break his heart, or if not break it, throw it open so widely, so completely, that he wouldn't ever be the same again.

It was the same thing, wasn't it?

He turned to the kitchen, eyed the cold breakfast with total distaste. He scraped the nauseating mess back into the frying pan, poured himself a cup of coffee and leaned against the bar, lost in thought.

He knew it wasn't the thought of reheating the breakfast that made him feel ill. It was remembering what Connie at FBI headquarters in Lubbock had told him about Winslow's latest victim, a twenty-six-year-old Denver airport beautician. Winslow had smothered her with one of her own plastic cover-ups and, in his now familiar perversion, had pasted a photograph of Kelsey over her face.

No message could have been more clear.

When the phone rang, he scarcely jumped. He simply flicked open the tracer, waited for it to activate, then picked up the receiver.

He nodded twice before he realized that Connie couldn't see him. He thanked her for calling and replaced the receiver. He should have guessed, he thought.

Winslow was using his name.

FBI agent John Chandler had stayed in the Dallas Hilton the night before. The call had been traced from his room. And now he was coming after Bill Winslow's ex-wife, who was being protected by Agent John Chandler.

The irony, the sheer audacity, was amazing. For Winslow, using John's own name, was now coming after the same John who had slept with Kelsey, had now felt his entire life called into question, and most of all, had, for the first time in his life, felt that budding promise of tomorrow flicker for a moment on the far distant horizon.

Well, he thought grimly. The fake John Chandler was going to have a little surprise waiting for him. The real Mc-Coy could be just as ruthless as his nasty counterpart.

Chapter 10

Friday, November 12
11:45 a.m., Lubbock, Texas

Alone in her bedroom behind the locked door, Kelsey checked, cleaned and reloaded her .38 automatic and tucked it into her holster. She waited for that feeling of security, of safety to steal over her, but it didn't come. She hadn't worn her gun in two days, not since John had arrived on her doorstep.

Now the .38 felt heavy, awkward, cumbersome. Was it really the gun, or was it some part of her that now saw the weapon in a different light?

She'd known that giving up her anger for passion would alter her, had known it would cost her, but hadn't realized how far-reaching those changes, those costs, would be.

Now, when she should be her very toughest, her most vigilant, all she could seem to feel was a pervasive sorrow that she'd once again lowered her guard for a moment. She couldn't afford the luxury of placing her heart in a man's hands.

She could tell herself all day that John was as different from Bill as bananas were from pasta, but John was still a man, and she knew only too well how trusting *any* man was the surest road to personal hell.

Still, there was something about John that touched her, and touched deeply. Too deeply perhaps. There was a thread of sorrow that ran through him, offset the slightly offbeat sense of humor, contrasted too harshly with the gentle touch of his hands. Was it this that allowed them to come together, the fact that he had known great pain and fear, too?

Until last night, she'd seen herself as wholly focused on survival, on day-to-day existence, with the eventual hope of embarking on a journey for the future, whatever that might prove to be. But under John's careful touch, coming alive at his kiss, she'd understood, perhaps for the first time since her initial shock at discovering her husband had hired someone to kill her, that she hadn't been planning for the future. She had been planning for only one moment of it, the moment she and Bill Winslow would again cross paths.

She had fought, struggled daily, to shed the old Kelsey, to build a strong, independent woman from the ashes. But that slow, deliberate construction hadn't been to ensure a tomorrow, just a single, desperate encounter. She could see that all too clearly now, and was afraid of it. Afraid of how it made her feel, especially in light of the night before.

That encounter was at hand now. And yet, conversely, tomorrow seemed the most precious of all things. Her adrenaline was high, her body fit and ready, and she had help waiting downstairs. But where was the sense of justification? Where was that surety that should accompany the tingling nerves, the jangling fears?

It was, she thought with some discomfort, noticeably absent. Because there was no future planned beyond that moment in time. Was that why last night had seemed so unbelievably perfect? In John's arms, under his loving regard, she could forget the present for a moment, ignore the past and cast a thin line of hope to a vague and nebulous future.

But it was a future that he didn't believe in, either. She could see it in his face, feel it in his distance. He, like she, didn't live for tomorrows. Only the present. He was a man to whom the future was only a vague concept, another assignment, another plane ticket, another poor soul to save.

Glancing in the mirror, she wondered what John saw when he looked at her. Was it the frightened woman of three years ago? The staunchly independent warrior? Or did he see something of both of those women in her personality? Or was there a different image altogether of the woman who'd been in his arms last night?

Because she felt wholly different now, and saw him differently as well. Never again would she be able to look at him and see only the FBI agent assigned to her case. Never again would he be the nameless, faceless stranger as he'd once, oh, so long ago called himself. He would now and forever be John Chandler, the man who had awakened her from a long and restless sleep.

But in the Sleeping Beauty fairy tale, the prince had stayed, or at least the story had led the reader to believe this was the case. This man was no Prince Charming. He had little use for conversation and less for tact. He was duty bound, and constricted by the very laws he sought to uphold.

And yet his mouth had told her volumes last night, his hands had created a symphony of beauty and his eyes had spoken every intimate, magical word ever dreamed of by a maid whose heart had been broken too many times, whose finger had been pricked on the spinning wheel of justice and whose sleep had been that of self-imposed strength.

So why didn't she feel strong now?

Her reflection only stared back, wide-eyed, as uncertain as she.

And then it came to her, the reason for the uncertainty, the cause of her confusion. In the feelings he inspired in her, in the trust he'd all too easily drawn from her the night before, John had stolen her anger, sapped her resolve.

In the mirror, her reflection stood a little straighter, her jawline tightened and her shoulders squared. Somehow, in the past thirty-six hours, since he'd stepped through her front gate, John Chandler had swept away her determination for a showdown with Bill Winslow. He'd made it seem unlikely, improbable, maybe even silly.

It *wasn't* ridiculous. It *wasn't* unthinkable. It was a matter of necessity. Like her anger. It was a matter of fact. Bill was coming to kill her, had killed three people, maybe more, in his eagerness to do away with her.

And she'd allowed herself the luxury of leaning on John, of forgetting what Bill would do to her if he did get through the team waiting outside, did get past John. She'd wallowed in the tomorrowless trust John had sparked in her the night before. She'd questioned her motives, her desperate needs, and had stood here wondering about futures. She'd even allowed the mind-crippling fear to seep into her body, infuse her veins with ice, because she'd *forgotten* her need to rid the world of Bill once and for all.

She remembered now. And if she refused to let memories of last night enter her mind, if she firmly squelched the ready recognition that sprang all too swiftly to her mind at the mere thought of his name, of his face...his touch...she would be able to see this through.

She hadn't lied to John. She'd meant every word she'd said to him earlier, she *did* want it finished forever. She couldn't live this way anymore. But, for the first time, she'd said it not from any misplaced anger, but from the remembrance of their night together, spilling the truth from the too short intimacy they had shared.

When the knock at her door was followed by John's voice, she only turned to answer the door. She told herself she wasn't looking at the carefully made-up bed. She was fairly sure she wasn't spending too much time seeing his shirt draped over the back of her incidental chair. And she was quite convinced that she'd already forgotten the torn foil wrappers in the bedside wastebasket.

She turned the lock on the door when she heard his voice. And knew, when she saw his face, that if she believed any of the hogwash she'd been trying to feed herself, she might just as well put an offer in on a slightly used bridge in California.

John searched her features for any resemblance to the woman who had shared his life last night. He noted the gun strapped to her hip, the squared shoulders. What did that have to do with anything? he wondered, seeing as how he was also wearing a shoulder holster, was himself tense with anticipation, tight with controlled energy.

He probed her eyes, hoping to see something of the trust he'd engendered throughout their passionate night, wanting to see a measure of something besides her too-careful anger.

He saw what he'd seen in his own eyes a hundred different times, that eagerness to resolve a case, an awareness of the inherent dangers, and something more, a question perhaps. A question that begged to know the next step, that demanded a reward, a promise that when this was over, everything would turn up roses.

It will, he wanted to tell her, needed to tell her. But he couldn't. Not only because he wasn't some crystal ball reader who could predict a happy outcome, but because he had never really been able to believe in rosy futures himself.

But studying her now, warrior to warrior, lover to lover, he found he'd never wanted anything so much in his whole life. What had she said about friends, that they were there for the high as well as the low points in life? A pizza and an evening spent together? There was so much more than that he wanted to give her, to tell her about. But there was too little time and he had nothing to give, nothing concrete to offer.

Especially not when what she wanted most in life was diametrically opposed to what he stood for. She wanted to kill Bill Winslow when and if he should arrive. That he might want the same thing was irrelevant. He was honor and duty bound to arrest the man, hand him over for the courts to mete out justice. But why was it that her way seemed to make so much sense?

"I need to know everything you think Bill might do," he said. "You were married to him, you know how he thinks. What is he likely to do next?"

He saw her eyes flatten slightly, assimilating his question, trying to fit it into the pattern of what was going on in their lives that morning.

"He wasn't in Lubbock when he called," she said slowly, almost a question.

"No. Dallas." He pictured the two cities, both Texan, so different from each other as to be located in other countries. One consisting of tall towers and bustling ambition, the other a sprawling land possessing wide lawns and slow-talking citizenry.

He had once been unable to picture Kelsey in Lubbock, and now found he could scarcely see her anywhere else. Like the desert painting over her bed, like the city she lived in, Kelsey was both lonely and strong, vulnerable and venerable with ancient knowledge. And she had a quirky sense of humor that seemed appropriate for the desert, a little dry, a bit crusty.

She drew a deep breath. "I don't think he'd use a commercial airline to get to Lubbock. By now, he would already have conned someone into flying them here in a private plane."

"That's good. I'll call the local airport and alert them. We'll put a couple of people out there to watch for him."

"You won't recognize him."

"We'll check everyone getting off a plane."

She smiled bitterly. "He'll think of something."

"So will we," John said, and his words were more a vow than a simple statement of fact. But were they a vow for the assignment or a personal pledge to Kelsey?

He didn't know and could tell by the puzzled look in her eyes that she didn't, either.

"Do you like to fish?" he asked.

She half smiled at his non sequitur, but didn't answer.

"Because if you do..." he continued, striving to sound casual, trying to tell himself that this wasn't a headlong leap into an uncertain future, only something to ease the shadows in her gaze. Just something between friends. "A friend of mine has a pretty tidy boat docked in North Carolina. We could take it out for a few days."

Her smile broadened, and despite the rather wistful quality of that gesture, he took heart.

"I think I'd like that," she said.

"It's a date, then," he answered, and felt they were doing things backward. They had already argued, already made love, already strapped their guns on to fight the bad guy, and now they were making dates? He had to smile.

She smiled back, easier this time, less wistfully.

"Okay, now," he said, "I want to see what you can do. If we're in this thing together, and Lord knows we are, I want to know just how you move, how you react."

A saucy light sprang into her beautiful eyes. "Oh, I think you know that fairly well."

He chuckled and felt as though a weight were rolling from his shoulders. What a hell of a team they made. What a team they could make. And at that thought, he knew he was wrong, the weight hadn't lifted, only changed position. It wasn't on his shoulders anymore; it lay heavy on his heart, making him feel slow and confused.

"Can you flip me?" he asked, then tried thinking of another way to phrase it.

"You or anyone else," she promptly replied.

He grinned again. This was his Kelsey. But why did the thought make him feel sad and more than a little angry?

"Show me," he said.

"Anytime," she answered.

"How about now?"

She didn't answer. She merely stepped forward, shot out a hand and gave a short, bloodcurdling yell. He was on his back in less time than it would have taken to tell about it. He looked up at her from the floor, not wondering how he got there, but how he was ever going to bear to leave her when all this was over.

"That what you had in mind?" she asked, leaning over him.

It wasn't what he had in mind at all.

Friday, November 12
2:50 p.m., Lubbock, Texas

There were at least four people watching her house. One hanging from a telephone pole, one in a car across the broad street from her house, a third in the skimpy bushes in the alley behind her place, and, he suspected, a fourth in one of the nearby houses. The neighbor's RV, if he had to make any guesses.

That would leave one, maybe two agents in her house.

Not too terribly bad odds.

Because they had an entirely different set of rules to live by than he did. They would take him alive at all costs. That's what they were supposed to do. They were the "good" guys. He chuckled, a raspy sound.

He didn't have to live by those rules. They were utterly expendable, mere obstacles to his objective—Kelsey. He thought about what he would do to her. He'd make her pay for the past three years, for not doing as he needed of her three years ago.

He sighed heavily, almost lovingly.

He would have to wait, because right now those agents were in his way. But, like waitresses or taxi drivers he would never see again, he didn't need to worry about their favor.

He lifted the binoculars to his eyes. He could see her house—her ostentatious, Spanish-style hacienda—as if it were close enough to reach out and touch the creamy stucco, grab hold of those succulent plants and climb straight up to those barricaded second-story windows.

He'd lived behind bars long enough to recognize the difference between what kept people out and what held people in. These bars were the comfortable variety. Easy. A piece of cake.

He lowered the field glasses and leaned back. A moan behind him caught his attention. He turned around and faced the woman tied up and gagged on the flowery love seat.

"Aren't you glad you weren't married to me?" he asked. He laughed as she hesitated before nodding.

Friday, November 12
4:30 p.m., Lubbock, Texas

The phone rang and Kelsey and John both froze. She looked at him with a sharp question in her fine gaze. He nodded slowly and, with her, crossed to the bar. He activated the tracer and flipped the listening switch before she lifted the wall receiver.

"Hello?" she asked. Her rich, sultry voice was at odds with her wide eyes, the tense grip of her hand. She might be tough, but she was also frightened nearly out of her wits.

Her eyes flashed to John's as the masculine voice came through the phone lines.

"You sound just fine, sweetheart. Are you ready for me? I'll be there soon. Very soon."

Winslow hung up with one of those dry chuckles, but not, John noted with grim satisfaction, before the tracer had locked in on his location.

Kelsey replaced the receiver and walked away from the bar, leaned against the glass of the patio doors. He wanted to tell her to get back from the glass, to hide in the house somewhere. But due to the construction of the veranda, the wide overhang and the broad patio itself, she was as protected there as she would be in the kitchen. And there was a man in the alley and one on the phone pole just a couple of blocks down.

He punched in the Lubbock office number and quickly gave the coordinates the tracer had logged. He said he'd hold for the verbal location and watched Kelsey closely while he did so.

She didn't look particularly frightened now, only thoughtful. Her blue eyes roamed the backyard, the broad expanse of trimmed grass, the succulents lining the walls, the still-green honeysuckle vines draped over the back end of the high adobe walls. She almost appeared to be considering what to plant in the spring, so quiet was her gaze.

He wanted to touch her, if nothing else, just to rest his hand on her shoulder, convey his sympathy, his assurance that all would be well. But he knew she didn't want his sympathy and he could scarcely assure her of something he wasn't any too sure about himself. And if he were totally honest, if he touched her, he wasn't sure he could stop.

Her eyes lifted to the rich blue sky, a vast expanse of cloudless beauty. She smiled slightly and he wished he knew what she was thinking.

"The call originated at the private airfield in Lubbock," the voice said over the line.

He ordered a report from the three men they'd placed at the small airport. It would be forthcoming, his contact said.

He hung up and didn't look at Kelsey as he advised her, "You were right." He told her where the call had come from. She didn't move, didn't seem to acknowledge his statement.

But after a moment, she asked, "Why don't I believe that?"

John was nonplussed. What could he say to that? "Why not?"

She shook her head and looked back out the window.

John thought she wore the identical expression she'd had the morning of Bill Winslow's trial for conspiracy to commit murder, the morning she'd discovered her life was only worth a handful of years.

The phone rang again and he almost forgot to switch on the tracer. He picked up the receiver this time, and handed the listener to Kelsey.

It was Connie with the report that the agents at Lubbock airport had called in. Four planes had landed there that morning and early afternoon. All disembarking passengers and pilots had checked out.

"The call came from there," he said.

"From one of the private planes. At least that's what we thought."

"Thought?"

"Cellular phone," Kelsey said dully.

And it clicked into place. The Secret Service was doing a lot of work these days with cellular phones. Because of the home-base requirement, a cellular phone could be used anywhere, but it recorded only from the point of origin. In other words, Winslow had used the phone, but certainly not necessarily from the Lubbock airport. He didn't have to be anywhere near the plane.

"How about the pilot?"

"They're taking him to the hospital now. He's still alive, but barely."

"And no one saw him? Winslow?"

"He left the plane as the pilot, with the pilot's ID. We didn't find the pilot until later."

John didn't have to ask how much later. After the phone call. He cursed himself for not having ordered that team to inspect each plane before letting anyone go. His brain wasn't functioning the way it should, he thought. He had too many other things on it, things that had nothing to do with this case. Had only to do with Kelsey.

There were good, solid reasons not to get involved with someone you were covering, he thought grimly, reminding himself a little too late.

"Will the pilot live?" Kelsey asked quietly.

John relayed the question to Connie, who said, "He has a good chance, the medics say. He was still breathing, and no vitals were hit."

"Weapon?"

"Knife."

John told her to call immediately with any new developments, then added, "Surely there's some way to get a fix on a C-type phone. Call the Secret Service. One of them might know some trick. Let me know the soonest." He hung up, and Kelsey did the same.

"I've gotta say this, Kelsey," he said grimly.

She only looked at him with that same dull expression. He couldn't read it, didn't think anyone would be able to.

"This is an operation now. Pure and simple. And we're going to treat it like one."

"No more fun and games?" she asked, the saucy look back in place.

He grinned, but said, "That's right. Game time's over."

"What a pity," she drawled. "And we were having such fun today."

She turned her back on him, missing his appreciative grin. She walked across the living/dining room toward the stairs. He called her name softly and she stopped.

He said slowly, ''As long as you know that nothing about last night was a game to me.''

Kelsey didn't wait for more, though she was sure that if he'd been able to see her face, he would have known how direct a hit he'd made—a flusher, or whatever boxers called that direct cut to the stomach, the one that knocked every single bit of wind from the opponent.

How the hell was she supposed to think angrily, even objectively or rationally, when he said things like that? When he'd now driven it home that what they had shared wasn't merely a distraction, something that had taken his mind momentarily from the task at hand?

She wanted to yell back down at him that it hadn't been any game for her, either, but that was coming too close to the truth, a truth she didn't dare examine now.

Friday, November 12
8:15 p.m., Lubbock, Texas

The man on the telephone pole wasn't hard to take out. He responded exactly as Bill had hoped he would to a curious neighbor's request for information.

''You been up on that pole off and on for a couple of days now,'' he said, calling up to the agent. He let a note of suspicion creep into his voice. ''You want to tell me what's going on?''

The man told him it was a problem with the long-distance phone lines.

He allowed suspicion to grow even greater. ''A problem that takes three days and as many men to correct?''

''You know how these things can be,'' the man called down with a smile.

Bill didn't smile back. "Well, how about showing me some ID, pal?"

When the man tried waving him away, he told the guy he thought the police just might be interested in a bunch of grown men hanging around telephone poles with binoculars around their necks.

He stomped away, the very picture of indignation, right in through the open back door of Kelsey's tied-up neighbor.

And he did call the police. And in typical right hand not letting the left know what was going on, the police arrived in three units and swarmed the "good" guys.

Bill laughed watching the exchange of badges, the searchlights strafing the alleyways.

He turned to the woman bound with her own housecoat tie. "My hallmark has always been the KISS theory? Do you know it?"

She shook her head, tears in her eyes.

"Keep It Simple, Stupid. Let me tell you, honey, it works every time."

Friday, November 12
8:30 p.m., Lubbock, Texas

John swore as he saw the commotion in the street. "Cover's blown," he muttered aloud, although Kelsey couldn't possibly have heard him in the next room. Some do-gooder neighbor, he thought, then on the heels of that condemnation came the chilling awareness that it could have been Winslow who'd tipped the police, who had used all the resources at hand to good—or bad—advantage.

The more he thought about it, the more he thought it might be Bill. He remembered the brief call from George, the poor guy on the telephone pole. "Some neighbor hassling me," he'd said, "didn't believe I was with the phone company. Said he was calling the police."

Now John wondered which neighbor, which house. "Kelsey?" he called. She'd know. She'd be able to tell them which neighbor was likely to get irate, which would have called in the police.

She stepped behind him, as soft footed as any agent. "Tell me about your neighbors," he said.

"I told you the first day," she answered.

"Yeah, yeah. But I mean those habit kind of details you were talking about. Who would have hassled George on the telephone pole, then called the police in to investigate?"

She frowned. "Mrs. Petersham—"

"Male."

"Mr. Anderson, across the street. I can't really picture him doing it, but he's often suspicious of strangers."

"What's he look like?"

"Oh, tall, white haired. Mustache. He was a colonel in the Korean War. Limps."

John jerked up the telephone and swore again as it rang without response. George was probably down on the ground now, talking with the police.

"Who else?" he asked.

"Well, Eloy Valencia. He's one of the city councilmen. He's friendly, but likes to know what's going on in the neighborhood."

"Looks?"

"Short—five six or so. Round. Black hair. Wears thick glasses."

"Good," he said, jotting this down in the notebook he'd taken from her highboy what seemed months ago. "Who else?"

"Gregory Adams. But I think he's blind. Diabetes. His wife has to do all the driving, everything."

"Old guy?"

"Yes. In his late seventies, early eighties, maybe."

"Okay. Anyone else?"

"I don't know too many people on the next block," Kelsey said. She sounded apologetic. "Just the people within my area. We have a sort of informal Neighborhood Watch."

"How about behind you? Across the alley?"

"They call it widow's row," she said. "All three of the women on that side of the block are widows."

"Do they have any sons, or even brothers who might go outside to investigate? Someone hassled Gordon, and he was out in the alley. Down about four houses."

"I don't know about sons. I've never really seen any men around them, except their lawn boys. Or maybe someone working on their roof."

"This could just be a case of Neighborhood Watch in action," he said. He pulled back the curtain to show her the activity in the street. "We're blown out of the water. At first I thought it might be Winslow, but if you have a Neighborhood Watch program, somebody might have called in."

"It's Bill," she said. Her voice was cold, emotionless. She might have been talking about the weather for all that she allowed inflection to shade her tone. Although, he thought, he'd never heard just that note of iciness, of implacability coming from her before. Anger, yes; suspicion, fear. And passion, he'd heard that. But not this dull chilled quality.

"Okay, let's assume it was. That means he's tagged everyone," he said. He peered through the curtain again, this time looking at the RV next door. "Except our—damn."

"The agent in the Bilby's RV?" she asked, as though she'd expected it.

"Yeah. That tears it." He dropped the curtain back into place. "From here on out, no windows, no doors under any circumstances. I don't want you five feet from me, do you have that? Unless we hear something and then I want you to do *exactly* what I tell you. No arguments, not even a peep. Clear?"

"Crystal," she said coldly.

He studied her for a moment, hating that icy note in her otherwise sultry voice. Her features were perfectly still, as though chiseled from pure marble. She was pale, and her lips were dry. But she didn't look frightened. Only cold. So very, very cold.

"And the idea is to catch him, not kill him."

"The idea is to survive," she contradicted.

"The *idea* is for *both* of us to survive," he fired back.

"Both who? You and I, or all three of us . . . you, me and Bill Winslow? Not the coziest of trios."

He surprised her when he laughed. "You're right, there. But we're still going to do everything we can to keep you safe, *and* take him alive."

"What if he doesn't want to play by your rules?"

John didn't answer her. He couldn't. If Bill Winslow was as hell-bent as he'd proven, then all bets were off. Protecting Kelsey was the only objective. The only priority. Everything else—including memories of her in his arms—was of no consequence.

And as he watched her leave the room, back straight, head regal, hips swaying in rhythm to her precise footsteps, he suddenly realized it wasn't a matter of protecting her life, it was a matter of preserving it. And preservation indicated a notion of future.

But which notion was that . . . and what on earth was he supposed to do about it now?

Chapter 11

Kelsey managed to clear the doorway and step into the hall before her icy facade melted. She couldn't seem to halt the sudden hot tears in her eyes, the shaking in her insides.

She was so very frightened, felt so very alone.

Hold me, she wanted to beg John, *just hold me.* Tell me any lie, any half-baked promise, just don't turn your back on me.

The hallway seemed to stretch forever in front of her, blurred by her tears, made longer by her complete lack of sustaining anger. She made it to her room by sheer will, but it was a willpower all too eroded, erased by the hard lines on John's face, the distance in his voice. How could someone change that much?

Or was it she who had changed?

This confrontation with Bill Winslow was still all important. It meant her very life, but so much more rested on it now. Before she had seen him as an impenetrable barrier to her ever having a sane and stable life. Now that she knew what that life could mean, sanity and stability didn't seem to matter. Those qualities seemed unimportant.

She hadn't been living; she'd been *existing*. More than ever, she wanted this struggle with Bill Winslow over. Because now, for the first time, she'd had a taste of what life could really be like. With John. He represented an altogether different perspective. A *future* perspective.

But he was rejecting it. She saw it in his eyes, heard it in his tone.

She'd loved one man wrongly, had suffered for it for thirteen years. And now John had opened the door for her to live again, to love again.

She told herself that this was impossible, she couldn't be wrong again. She could love John Chandler. Fate wouldn't be so unfair as to have her fall in love with a man to whom the future was only a pipe dream, a man to whom the present was the be-all and end-all of existence. And a man who could turn on and off the faucet of affection like anyone else drew water.

Was she in love?

If she wasn't, this was hell. It was hell, anyway.

She made it through her bedroom door, feeling the hot tears of loneliness, of fear, coursing down her cheeks. She was glad he hadn't seen them. Was afraid that if he had, he would only have turned away, as he had this afternoon, as he had only moments before.

He'd said that he didn't know what to say to her about last night; he hadn't talked much then, either. Now, today, without any words, without his touch, she felt cast adrift. He'd cut her off from her anger, her driving need for vengeance, and left her where? Out in the dark somewhere, trapped in a world of hurt, a universe of unanswered questions.

Her knees buckled and she slumped to the floor, not even reaching the bed. She buried her face in her hands, trying to stem the flow of anguish, having no success. The tears burned, hot and scalding, coming not from her eyes but from her heart. When had she last cried, really *cried* the tears that come from the soul, the depths of the heart, the lowest point of despair?

Three years ago in a dreary apartment in downtown Lubbock. Those tears had been cleansing. These were tears of longing, tears of abject loneliness. Why couldn't he just hold her? Set aside the agent's tough exterior, take her into his broad arms and hold her tightly, as a man, a lover?

"Why?" she sobbed aloud, aching for the feel of him, crying for his loss.

John tried George again, hung up the phone in disgust. It was anybody's game now. He heard a muffled sound from the hallway, as if Kelsey had stumbled and braced a hand against the wall for support. He didn't hear it repeated and started to make another call when he heard another sound, a dull thud from her bedroom.

Curious, feeling the adrenaline course through him in sudden fear, he held his hand over the butt of his gun and went down the short hallway. He stopped in the doorway, feeling as though someone had shot him.

Kelsey was on her knees, body bent forward, her face in her hands, crying. Crying as if her very soul were torn apart and not all the king's horses, nor any of the Bureau's men, could put it together again.

"Why?" he heard her sob.

He dropped his hand from the gun, stood there indecisively for what seemed a century, but was less than a second. Then he stepped forward, dropped beside her and swept her into his arms. Nothing on the face of the earth could have stopped him. Not the job, not duty, not even a bullet from Bill Winslow.

He pulled her roughly against his chest, holding her shaking form with both arms, his hands pressing her to him. She resisted, but it was no more resistance than a child who had been hurt would pull away from a kind touch, a gentle voice. She buried her head against him, sobbing harder.

He felt as if every tear was searing him, burning him, melting some essential part of him. She had been so cold only moments before. Hiding this from him, he thought now, and knew he was right.

"Ah, Kelsey..." he murmured against her silky hair. "Don't cry...please don't cry."

If anything, she cried harder.

He did the only thing he knew how to do—envelop her with his legs, his arms, the emotions he couldn't name, and rock her slightly. Over and over he murmured her name and simply held her, aching for her, some part of him crying with her, giving her time, letting her sob it out.

The tears didn't come strictly from fear. He knew that as well as he knew anything. They had come from him. He'd caused them. From his keeping her at a distance to his barking orders at her as though she were some incompetent flunky. Couldn't she see how frightened he was for her? This wasn't just a case. It was her *life*. He'd already screwed up by getting involved. Anything he did now, any mistake he made in the next few days, possibly hours, could mean that Kelsey wouldn't be around to see that tomorrow she seemed to want. For her sake, he'd had to shut her out.

But had he really needed to? He questioned it now, holding her, and wondered if that shutting out had as much to do with his fear of dealing squarely with the emotions she sparked in him as his fear of having something happen to her.

It was both, he decided, and knew that the two seemingly different viewpoints had fused into one jumbled mass that could only spell disaster.

"P-promise me," she whispered raggedly.

He murmured her name, making it a promise in and of itself.

"Promise me..." she said again, louder this time. Clearer.

"What do you want me to promise?" he asked. His heart seemed to stop beating while he waited for her answer.

"I don't know," she said on a sob. "Just something. Anything. Don't leave me out here in the dark, wondering. Hoping you'll give me some sign that last night mattered. That you won't turn your back on me. Tell me something important, something I can hold on to when this terrible, terrible fear sweeps in and makes me want to scream, makes me crazy with the waiting. Just *hold* me. Promise me."

John felt she had plunged a knife into him. His arms tightened around her convulsively. He had to look up, blinking furiously against the sudden sting in his own eyes. Didn't she know she was asking for *everything?* Didn't she know she was breaking his heart? That she was the one making *him* crazy?

"I'm here, Kelsey. I'm here," he said. And though she didn't ask, he could almost taste her next question. *But for how long?* He couldn't answer, not her, not himself.

And so he merely held her, rocked her, waited for her tears to subside, feeling as if every tear belonged to him, had his name indelibly etched in the salty water.

He thought about her promise, her poignant demand for him to keep the shadows at bay, to haul her in from the cold he'd placed her in with his distance. And he thought about her vow to kill Bill Winslow, to end his torment once and for all.

And for a long, hard moment, he thought of promising her this, to do the job for her. To take the law in his own hands, to calmly, coldly, kill her ex-husband. Everything in him, all he had fought for these twenty-odd years, struggled against this notion, screamed a denial, but he quelled the rage by reminding himself this was Kelsey he was thinking about, it was *Kelsey*.

But taking the law into his own hands, locking her safely in a closet while he went downstairs, found a good solid corner, and sat waiting for Bill Winslow with the one thought of killing him was the height of *wrong*. If he did that, he couldn't possibly ever pretend he was doing it out of love for Kelsey, or out of some misguided penance for having hurt or abandoned her in the past. He would be doing it in payment for her tears, in atonement for every deed Winslow had done to her, to others. He would be killing him because he *hated* him, not because his job demanded that he do so.

And he wouldn't be the cold professional, he would be the hot-blooded avenger of this woman he cared too deeply for. He would be the lover who had roused her passion but stolen her anger, the man who wanted her to remember nothing but him, who would gladly, almost joyfully, kill the sordid reminder of her terrible past.

It would be wrong, he knew, but it felt so very right.

Friday, November 12
9:20 p.m., Lubbock, Texas

He couldn't be sure which room she was hiding in. The house was lit up like a Fourth of July party in full swing, even if all the curtains were drawn.

The little widow with the pink fuzzy housecoat had been only too happy to tell him the layout of Kelsey's house. She'd only been in it a few times, she'd stammered, but had seemed to remember it with some detail. If he went in the back door, the kitchen was to the right, open to the dining room right in front of him, the living room to his left. An exercise room was beyond that, where the Careys used to have their formal living area. Upstairs there were three bedrooms, one overlooking the front side of the house, the master on the east and a guest room overlooking the back of the house. Even with his help, she couldn't seem to remember how many bathrooms or closets there were on either of the floors.

She had babbled on about Mexican tile and plants, and a thousand meaningless nothings, until he gave her back her dishrag. It was also pink. "I've always had an eye for detail," he told her, patting her wet cheek.

There was no reason to have let her live, he thought now as he slipped from the shadows at the side wall to the shadows of Kelsey's patio. But he hated obvious patterns. Later, when it didn't matter anymore, people would wonder why he'd let the old woman live.

He liked that.

He smiled. Right now, he liked just about everything.

Chapter 12

Friday, November 12
10:00 p.m., Lubbock, Texas

John held Kelsey until his knees ached, until his back screamed for attention, and continued to hold her even then. She had stopped crying, had been silent for some time now. He half wondered if she was asleep.

She rid him of this question with her sigh and next words. "I'm sorry."

"Don't apologize," he said. "I'm the one who made you cry."

"Not you. Not really. It's just everything. I felt like the whole world had come crashing down on me, and I didn't know where to turn."

"You can always turn to me," he said. His voice seemed to catch in his throat, like a last-ditch effort to hold in a promise.

She didn't say anything for a long while and he wondered if she was mulling over his words or simply rejecting them.

''What are we going to do?'' she asked. Her voice was as rich as ever, yet sounded girlish in an odd way.

He didn't know if she was asking him about whatever strange relationship they had suddenly created, or if she was seeking some information about Bill Winslow.

Either way, there was nothing he could answer with, so he said instead, ''You're going to wash your face. Then we're going to go downstairs and I'm going to make us some coffee.'' He didn't add what he was thinking, that it was likely to be the longest night of their lives.

''Practical to the end?''

He smiled even as he frowned. She was something. How many other women could quip with him after crying as though there were no tomorrow . . . and knowing that might well be true.

''Kelsey . . .''

She stirred in his arms, but he wouldn't let her go, wouldn't let her pull away enough to look at him. Not until he said what he had to say.

''Last night—'' She stiffened, and he held her even tighter, willing her to let him finish, forcing himself to continue. ''It meant something to me, too,'' he said.

Somehow it didn't seem enough, didn't seem to cover a quarter of the ground he needed to talk about, needed to let her know. But he couldn't say more. This was far more than he'd ever told anyone before.

She relaxed a little but didn't say anything.

''Make love to me,'' she said.

He closed his eyes in sharp pain. God, didn't she know how much he wanted her? ''Kelsey, the bad guys are coming,'' he said raggedly, trying desperately to cling to sanity. ''We have to circle the wagons. We can't indulge—''

''Yes, we can,'' she interrupted. ''Indulge me.'' And before he could stop her—not that he fought her much—she leaned forward, pressing her lips to his.

He could taste the salt of her tears, the pain she'd felt shedding them. And there was nothing shy of Bill Winslow bursting through the opened bedroom door that could have made him resist her.

Their coming together wasn't a sweet and tender encounter, something slow and leisurely, achingly haunting. Without taking her lips from his, without interrupting their fierce kiss, her hands tore at his clothing, strafed his back, his shoulders, as if she couldn't get enough of touching him.

Driven by a compulsion equally demanding, he raked her body with his hands, pulling at her clothes, pressing her down to the carpet, never once pausing or hesitating. Relentless in his mind was the sharp awareness that this might be the last time he'd ever be with Kelsey, ever know the passion that seemed to spring so effortlessly from her body, her lips, her heart.

Time was meaningless but fueled with desperation. Their hearts pounded in thunderous capitulation, in a drive as ancient and primeval as the universe itself.

He ruthlessly pushed her bodysuit down over her shoulders, pinning her arms, and pulled her bra down swiftly, baring her to him. He swiftly shifted to draw a taut nipple into his mouth, suckled it with sharp need, transferred his attention to the other and repeated the action. Her moan in response shivered through him. He had to have her, had to make her his. Now.

He rose slightly, never losing contact with her breast, and dragged at that damned bodysuit with both hands. When her hands were free, she pulled him sharply to her, not waiting for the suit to be completely removed. She arched her legs and her hands swiftly unfastened his pants, reaching inside for him.

He met her hands with a groan of combined agony and relief. His mind screamed warnings of caution, of care. Lifting his head, he tried to think, fumbled for his wallet as she kicked her legs free of the suit. By some miracle, and with her impatient assistance, he managed to don the only sane element of their explosive coupling. He'd no more felt the thing in place when she ground him to her and opened to him fully, taking him deep inside her.

Her legs wrapped around him as though unwilling to let him escape. He had no intention of doing so. Fueled by anger at himself, fear over what might happen to Kelsey, and a need to erase all memory of her tears, of his own inability to understand what she incited in him, he drove into her. Deep, long, hard. She matched his thrusts with a rocking rhythm, pulling him to her and holding him tightly.

"You're...in...*now*," she gasped out.

He couldn't speak, could only growl out a ragged, raw acknowledgement of her truth. Her fingers dug into his back, her heels thrummed against his buttocks.

She cried out his name as the explosion hit them and she bucked against him sharply. She held him there, suspended, seemingly defying gravity, and he felt her muscles convulse around the exquisite agony of his release. She drew him deeper and more firmly to her, and then leaned her face into the hollow of his throat.

"John...John," she murmured, repeating his name over and over as if naming the feelings, the emotions after him. He understood completely.

He tried pulling away, but she wouldn't release him, wouldn't loosen her legs. He allowed her to hold him, resting his head against hers, wishing he could think of the right words to say, any words, some phrase or two that would set the world back to rights.

As usual, it was Kelsey who did so. She breathed into his ear, "Now, that's what I call circling the wagons."

"I've never been too much in the analyzing feelings department," he said. "But I wanted you to know that you got in."

She sighed heavily. "Will you tell me that again, later?" she asked.

Yep, one in a million. In a billion. So why was it so hard to articulate what he was feeling? Why couldn't he even admit it to himself? He thought about it and smiled wryly. Leave it to Kelsey to cut through any gray areas, continually on the search for the definitive black-and-white.

"If I can," he said.

"You'd better promise," she said harshly, though again, she didn't say what she wanted him to promise.

But he knew.

"Yeah," he said, but even to himself, he sounded doubtful.

Kelsey washed the tearstains from her face with a washcloth that smelled like John. She didn't feel foolish for her tears, her emotional outburst. She should have, she thought, but couldn't seem to feel other than relieved. She'd cried the tears that needed to be shed, uttered the words that needed speaking. And as he had twenty-four hours earlier, he'd let his touch speak for him, his hands convey the message his voice seemed unwilling to impart.

And he'd given her something new to think about, to worry about. Always before when she'd considered this confrontation with Bill, she'd viewed it in terms of only her and Bill. John had added a third element—himself. She knew from his few words, his fierce hold of her, that he would rather die than see her hurt. If there was the remotest chance of Bill getting through, John would go down rather than let him get to her.

Could she live with that? Could she wake up every morning for the rest of her life knowing that her anger, her insistence that they stay put, had caused John Chandler's death?

No. It was that simple. She couldn't possibly begin to face that. It would be the death of everything she knew to be good, to be honest. If he died because of her, she might as well be dead, too, for life wouldn't hold anything for her.

She wondered how long she'd been dodging this terrible concept and knew it had been at least since their kiss that first morning, possibly before then. And still she had pushed for the confrontation, the shoot-out, the final showdown.

Now it was too late to back out. Too late to skip down the hallway and announce, oops, she'd been a little crazy, that in her obsession with Bill, she'd forgotten about John, that she'd put him on the back burner of her mind, had ignored the dangers to him if not to herself. It was also too late to say she was sorry she'd forced the issue, demanded to stay put for a no-holds-barred old-fashioned gunfight.

And, in the wake of his admission, too late to admit that she loved him. Because now, with the danger to him so very clear in her mind, her awareness of what his life meant to her, she knew that it was true. She did love John Chandler. With everything she had.

She tossed the washcloth into the sink, smiling a little as it collapsed into a loose ball. This was hardly the time to worry about being tidy. She left the bathroom and rejoined John in her bedroom.

He looked distant, but smiled at her nonetheless. It was a shy grin, the kind a little boy might proffer a new kid on the block. Hesitant, reserved, yet strangely open, unguarded.

They went down the stairs together, and she felt almost no fear as he insisted on going first, his gun drawn and at the ready. The downstairs was quiet, still and shrouded in shadows.

He checked all the rooms—it didn't take long as only the exercise room and the kitchen were even marginally separate—and signaled her to come down. She did so with a smile, though she didn't meet his eyes.

She didn't want him to read her newfound fears. Somehow, letting him see that, letting him read her love for him, smacked of telling him that she thought they might fail in their attempt to stay alive.

"Are you going to call for backup?" she asked.

"Don't have to," he said. He jerked his head toward the front door. "For all that their cover is blown, they're all still there, and keeping twice as close an eye on the place."

She felt immeasurably relieved. Bill might have called the police—assuming it *had* been him and not some other helpful neighbor—he might have exposed the hiding places of the FBI, but he hadn't managed to chase them away.

She wished now, fervently, that one of them would spot him, would arrest him before he ever so much as saw her. John was right, he was up on murder one now. He wouldn't just get a slap on the wrist for that, would he?

Knowing the justice system as she bitterly did, she was half-afraid he would. Which meant that the nightmare would start all over again in a few years. But at least, that way, she would be sure that John would be alive to tell about it.

That was, until his next assignment. Only, what did *that* matter? She wouldn't be with him, then, either.

The phone, their harbinger of nothing but bad news, pealed, making both of them jump. As if they had rehearsed their routine, Kelsey went for the wall receiver as John handled the tracer. At his signal, she lifted it.

The person on the other end didn't wait for Kelsey's greeting. "You've got to get out of there right now!" a woman's nearly hysterical voice quavered in her ear.

Kelsey met John's eyes in quick question. He waved at her to continue.

"Who is this?"

"Jenny Stedman, but that doesn't matter! You've got to get out of that house. He knows you're there. He's been watching your place! Oh, God, honey, he's planning to kill you. Now, you listen to me, girl, and you get right out of there."

"Mrs. Stedman?" Kelsey pointed out the back patio doors for John's benefit. "Are *you* all right?" She emphasized the pronoun so the woman wouldn't think Kelsey was questioning her sanity.

"I've lived through two husbands, honey. I ain't going yet. But he's a lunatic, and he's at your place now."

"I'm fine, Mrs. Stedman," Kelsey said. It was all she could think to say. She didn't know if Bill was standing beside frail Mrs. Stedman holding a weapon on her, or if the older woman had managed to get free of him somehow.

John nodded. He depressed a switch Kelsey hadn't even known about, and patched through a call to the bureau. "Get someone over to—?" He shot Kelsey a sharply questioning look. She mouthed the answer. "To 1412 Las Mesas Drive. No, send one we've already got here. And tell him to go in carefully, our boy may be inside."

"Mrs. Stedman?" Kelsey asked. "John's sending someone over to take care of you."

"Don't worry about that," the woman said. "Just you mind and get clear of that place. *Pronto!* Oh, Lord, what now? There's someone banging on my door saying he's from the FBI."

"Tell her to have the agent identify himself," John said. Kelsey did as he commanded, thinking he couldn't get any paler. For all he knew, he was sending an agent in to his certain death.

"He says his name is George Adams," Mrs. Stedman said querulously.

John ran a hand through his hair. He grabbed the phone from Kelsey. "Is there anyone else with you?" he barked.

"No. That man, the one that's after Kelsey, left here about two hours ago."

"Can you walk, ma'am?"

"Yes, I can. As soon as I untie my legs. Twit tied me up with my own housecoat cord. Made me eat my dirty dishrag all afternoon."

John grimaced, though Kelsey half wondered if he wasn't trying to hide a nervous grin. "Let George in, ma'am. He'll take care of you."

"Fine by me. But when this is all over, whatever it is that's going on, I want somebody to tell me how it is that law-abiding citizens can get trussed up like a Thanksgiving turkey right in their own TV rooms. I'm coming. I'm coming. Don't knock the door down."

She hung up without a farewell. John turned to Kelsey, no longer bothering to hide his grin. "I think Winslow was lucky with that lady. She sounds like she could have had him for breakfast."

Kelsey smiled wanly. She couldn't imagine anyone harming Mrs. Stedman. She was eighty-three years old, maybe five-two or -three and as thin as the proverbial reed. She was half amazed her elderly neighbor hadn't died of a heart attack during the assault.

So many people hurt, she thought. Because of her. Because of Bill's warped notion of revenge, because of his single-minded desire to murder her.

As if he were reading her mind, John reached out and touched her shoulder, a gentle nudge. "It's not your fault," he said. "Winslow's a lunatic. Even our Mrs. Stedman realized it. You heard her. And she doesn't blame you, does she?"

"She should," Kelsey said.

"If you follow that line of logic," he said with a twisted smile, "it would be a grandparent's fault when a grandchild robs a store, a storekeeper's fault when an employee beats his wife. Like you told me, anyone that Winslow has hurt has only been in his way. You can be thankful he didn't kill Mrs. Stedman."

The phone rang again and they did their little routine, though Kelsey thought by now it more a matter of show than for any expectation of results.

"George, here. Mrs. Stedman's okay. A little shook up. I'm calling for an ambulance." There was a pause. "The department will pick up the tab, won't they? See, ma'am, I told you they would." He hung up, the sound of Mrs. Stedman's voice overriding his farewell.

Kelsey hung up the phone slowly. "How long did she say that Bill had been gone from her house?"

John frowned heavily. "Two hours."

She felt fate scratching at her mind. She'd wished for a showdown, demanded one. The adage of being careful what you wished for lest it come true, seemed all too eerily appropriate right now.

"Then where is he?" she asked.

Friday, November 12
10:30 p.m., Lubbock, Texas

He could have told them if they had taken a good look right from that kitchen window. He was cold, he was hungry and he was furious.

He should have killed the old lady, after all. Who would have thought someone who didn't look as though she could bend over and put on her own shoes could have managed to get untied and call Kelsey, and thus, the FBI?

He should have been in the house a long time ago. But that damned Chandler had rigged every window, every door.

It wasn't really that big of a problem, he decided. Extreme obstacles only required extreme thought. And he was a genius. He could do *anything*.

And he knew one thing the old lady had forgotten to tell Kelsey's FBI boyfriend. She'd given him, after only a couple of polite requests, her husband's Colt .45, the great leveler. He would enjoy seeing the look on Kelsey's face when he used it on lover boy.

He relaxed. He wasn't cold anymore. And his hunger wasn't for food.

The game was about to go into high gear. It would be fun. Because he was free.

Extremely free.

Saturday, November 13
2:00 a.m., Lubbock, Texas

"If I have one more cup of coffee, I'll never be able to hold a gun steady," Kelsey said. She held out her hand for him to see. It wasn't trembling in the slightest.

John shot her a hard look. "As far as I'm concerned, you won't be using that gun of yours."

"Tell me that when Winslow bursts in," she countered.

He grinned wearily. "You know, if I didn't know better, I'd say you were Bureau trained."

"When a person's scared enough, they can find the right places to learn a few tricks," she said.

He chuckled. What was it about her that made him want to smile even as she turned him upside down with anger and inside out with longing?

He felt they'd been waiting a lifetime for some kind of movement from Winslow. Maybe the show of force outside earlier hadn't been Winslow's idea, maybe all that firepower had chased him away. The notion was dual edged, making him wish that were the case, and hope like hell it wasn't. The first because he was bone tired and would give a month's salary to stretch out on Kelsey's bed, perhaps just tuck her head on his shoulder and sleep for at least a week. The latter because if they didn't catch Winslow now, he'd just keep coming. And keep coming until he eventually got Kelsey.

That notion sobered him, woke him fully. If Winslow ever got his hands on Kelsey, she wouldn't stand a prayer. She might be all but professionally trained, but no amount of training in the world could stand up to a psychopath. He'd attended too many death-in-the-line-of-duty ceremonies not to know this was true.

If he didn't take care of Winslow, if the man got through, who would have a ceremony for Kelsey? Not the police. Not the FBI. She had no parents, no relatives. There would be no family to receive posthumous medals, a folded American flag, a rose to press in a family Bible. And if Winslow had gotten past him, there would be no John Chandler there, either, dressed in black, heart heavy with failed intention.

"What'll you do when this is all over?" he asked her. Let it be big, he prayed silently. Let her dreams be so sweeping, so all-encompassing, that he would be able to feel the reality of them, see them as she could.

Her blue eyes met his swiftly, assessingly, he thought. Not sizing him up, but rather to see if he was really interested. He nodded.

"I thought about that this afternoon. Or was it yesterday? It seems a lifetime ago, somehow. Anyway, I realized I hadn't ever really thought beyond today. Beyond a confrontation with Bill, I mean."

That struck him as inexpressibly sad. He wondered how many other people were out in the world that very minute, minds on the past, hearts on hold, just waiting for some kind of resolution to their lives. He asked gently, "And now?"

"And now I'm going to go get some more coffee," she said, averting her gaze, pushing to her feet. She stretched slowly, reaching for the ceiling, arching backward, straining forward. John swallowed heavily. Was she doing that on purpose?

He rose, also, stopping her, not from going downstairs, but from driving him insane. She turned to face him, her eyes meeting his. He could almost feel the electric current that sprang between them, ran like a spark from her arm through his hand and up.

There was so very much he wanted to tell her. So much he couldn't say. Didn't even know how to begin to say.

Her lips parted.

Without conscious volition, John pulled her into him, crushing her to his chest, molding her to his body. God, what was it about her that made him forget everything?

"This shouldn't be happening," she taunted, a saucy smile on her lips.

He hushed her in the oldest way known to man, by kissing her. His groan seemed to vibrate through every part of him, his chest, his legs, his hands. How could he even contemplate letting her go? He couldn't, and knew it. He wanted to drown in her scent, die at her touch.

She buckled in his arms, moaning softly, clinging to him as if he were the only sinecure in an otherwise topsy-turvy world. He knew the feeling. What was he to do with her? His life seemed to stretch before him, an endless stream of packed suitcases and other assignments. A lonely apartment on a beach somewhere, some unspecified time after retirement, a television on, a half-empty beer in his limp, bored hands.

A revulsion shuddered through him. He couldn't taste this, then go back to the long nights of nothing and no one. Worse, he would rather have no one than be without this.

He had to touch her, make certain she was real, that she was in his arms again, where he'd thought she would never be, could never be. Her fingers teased his hair, stroked his face, touched him not as a friend, not just as a lover. As a partner, a mate.

He heard a faint beep that stopped almost as soon as he raised his head. It was far too short to be one of the alarms. He was still for a moment, listening, but heard no other sound. It must have come from outside somewhere, he thought.

"You're going to give me a complex," she said, smiling at him, telling him otherwise with her candid gaze. "First yes, then no, then yes again. What's a girl to think?"

He showed her, grinding her to him. He wanted to take her right then and there and damn all consequences. But he couldn't. Her entire safety, her *life* was literally in his hands.

With an almost angry thrust, he shoved her away from him, held her at arm's length. "I can't think when you touch me," he said, knowing he was being unfair, knowing he'd started it but irrationally angry with her for so undermining his sense of duty, his complete awareness that all that stood between her and certain death was one very tired FBI agent who wanted her more than life itself.

She drew a deep breath. "There are lots of ways to hide, John," she said.

"What does that mean?" Though he thought he knew.

"It means you care just as much as I do. But you're not about to let me know it."

When he didn't say anything, only looked at her with agony and confusion filtering his brown eyes, she turned and left the room without saying anything else. What was there to say?

She had all but laid it on the line. She hadn't thought beyond today. Today was nearly over. She wanted him to give her a future, hand it to her on a proverbial platter. She had given him the lead-in and he had remained silent.

She *knew* he cared. No one could look at another human being the way he looked at her and not care down to his very core. And she knew that he was utterly confounded by the emotions she sparked in him.

That was only fair, she thought as she stomped down the hall. She cared, too. Too much. And too fruitlessly. Well, she'd be damned if she'd stand around waiting for him to tell her how swiftly he'd leave when the bell rang on this assignment. *If* the bell rang.

She had already started down the steps, so intent on her march she hadn't heard him come up behind her. He grabbed her arm, half whirling her around. She nearly lost her footing and rounded on him angrily.

"Let me go!"

"Damn it, I told you not to get outside of five feet from me. Remember?"

"You're the one who pushed me away, remember?"

"Not five feet!"

She couldn't help it. She chuckled.

He didn't so much as crack a smile, but his grip relaxed a little on her arm. "Okay. You win. But please, stay where I can cover you."

"Anytime," she quipped, lowering her voice almost a full octave.

John groaned, and his reluctant smile surfaced. "You're a menace," he said.

"As long as the FBI knows about it. . . ." she said.

"It's in my report," he shot back.

"Oh, I think it's probably in more than that. I remember you saying something about me getting in," she answered slowly. Meaningfully. No longer joking at all.

His eyes softened and he stepped down on the stair next to hers. The broad stairwell had never seemed so narrow before. She could feel the press of the curved stucco wall against her back, wanted to lean against it, letting its cool plaster absorb her sudden heat.

"Oh, you got in, all right. But I think I got in, too."

She opened her mouth and closed it again. His face was so close to hers she could have leaned forward a single notch and kissed him. She didn't. She only waited, staring at him half in anger, half in sorrow-filled hunger.

"Now let's get some damned coffee," he growled.

Neither one of them saw the shadow at the base of the stairs.

Chapter 13

Kelsey shook her arm free of John's hand and passed regally down the remaining stairs. She sailed through the darkened dining area and on into the kitchen, trying to think of some witty remark, something that would chase the confusion from his eyes, wipe the tension from his mouth.

Unfortunately, there was nothing *to* say. Not without simply asking him for a future he was unprepared to offer, a future she couldn't even begin to sketch out for herself, let alone him. And not without knowing that it was a moot question, anyway, considering the not inconsiderable circumstances.

She reached for the glass coffeepot, then set it down again, and smiled—evilly, she knew—and reached for the cabinet instead. She pulled out a bag of rice cakes, the driest, foulest tasting things she could think of, and turned to him, holding them up.

"Want one?" she asked.

He frowned, stepped into the doorway of the kitchen, half in and half out of the light, and looked down at what she held. A slow, almost rueful grin curved his lips. He met her gaze and shook his head. She found she'd been waiting for just that smile, just that look of reluctant humor.

Surely someone who could match her humor, could touch her soul, make her heart pound in ways it never had before, surely that someone should be part of her life, her love? Why hadn't she ever seen her life as empty before? Was it simply that he filled it so completely?

His shadow bounced on the wall behind him, spilled onto the stairs. She wanted to keep looking at John, but the shadow's erratic behavior claimed her attention.

And she knew without fully knowing. Her instincts screamed every warning that has ever been issued to a prey in the sights of the hawk.

Bill was there. *He was in her house!*

Without thinking, knowing only that the shadow danced *behind* John, that his very life depended on her next action, her alerting him to the danger, she simply acted. She threw the rice cakes at John with all her might.

As if in a dream, she saw his smile fade to a shocked question and saw him duck to avoid the flying plastic bag. His lips curved to say something, but whatever it might have been was drowned out by the deafening explosion of a handgun.

A sharp spasm of pain crossed his face as he dropped to the floor. The pain that had caused that look was magnified a hundred times in her heart. Not now, she screamed silently. *Not now!* Not when she had just discovered that life could have meaning, that futures could exist, that there was more to life than subsistence, more to living than survival.

Not dead, she thought frantically, dropping to her stomach and crawling toward him. She had pulled her gun on instinct, she found, but it was in her way now, impeding her progress to John. She didn't even think of using the weapon on the dancing shadow; she had only one objective: making certain John was alive.

"Well, well," a too-familiar voice said from the dining room.

Bill crossed the line of shadows and moved into the light. He smiled down at John first, then at her. He held a Colt .45 in his hands and it was trained on John.

He looked different, she thought wildly, then realized that, like her, he'd changed his hair color. Unlike her, she thought giddily, he'd killed his beautician. She had chosen black, a dark, strong color. He'd selected a wheaten blond. It rested oddly with his darkish features, lending him a tan he didn't possess—couldn't from his years in prison—and a Nordic quality she'd never seen in him before.

His smile was the same, but she could detect the ragged edges of his recent trek across the country. The fine veneer he'd always kept so polished, so perfectly in place, had eroded, perhaps in the past three years, more likely in the past three days. He was like a reproduction of an antique that someone had left too long in the weather. You could tell now that it wasn't priceless, could see the cracks in the wood, the stress at the joints.

All the lies were exposed now, she thought. Every last one of them.

And not one of them mattered a whit. Only John mattered. Time seemed to fold in on itself, freezing this moment, a stop frame in the continuum. It was his life flashing before her eyes, not her own. She could see him as she had the first time, the quiet, observant FBI agent who had met her eyes with sympathy as he'd told her that her husband had hired someone to kill her. She saw him as he read the newspaper accounts of her death, his face pinched and that telltale muscle in his jaw pulsing with suppressed emotion. She felt his first touch, that moment when comfort had metamorphosed to desire. She could smell his tangy aftershave, his particular heady male scent. And she remembered all the times she'd snapped at him, yelled at him, trying to prove to him that she was tough, could handle anything thrown her way.

She wanted to tell him now, make him understand, that she couldn't handle this. She couldn't handle his being hurt, couldn't possibly handle his death. Especially as it was a direct result of her recalcitrance, her need for ending Bill's threat over her.

She drew a deep, shuddering breath and was horrified to discover she could smell the sharp, coppery scent of blood.

"John?" she asked, never taking her eyes from Bill.

"I'm all right," he muttered. A relief such as none she'd ever known washed through her, making her almost sick with gratitude.

"Thanks to your warped sense of humor," he muttered.

Here they were, in the single most dangerous spot of their lives, and he was cracking jokes? The worst thing about it was that she wanted to smile. She wanted to do more than that. She wanted to laugh, cry, sing. Dance. *John was alive!*

She actually felt her lips curve into a slight smile. Was that what he was trying to tell her? Take heart, I'm all right. You're alive. We still have a chance. A slim one, but a chance.

She slowly pushed to a sitting position, almost surprised to find she still had her .38 in her hand. For all the good it would do her now. She was careful not to look at Bill, not to rile him, not to do anything that might make him fire that gun again. John, she noticed with admiration—and then sharp apprehension; was he really all right? Had he been hit in the back?—stayed where he was.

She wasn't afraid anymore, and yet was more scared than she'd ever been in her life. She wasn't afraid of Bill. He wasn't going to simply shoot her and call it quits. He'd gone too far, too terribly far, to end it so quickly now. His journal, his entire history, spoke to his need to torment. He would want to play with her a while, draw every nuance of terror from her.

But she *was* afraid for John. He would represent an obstacle, just something in the way. Like the medical supplies salesman, the doctor, the beautician, even the pilot and Mrs. Stedman. She tried taking heart from the fact that he hadn't killed any of the agents outside, merely called the police on them, but then she couldn't even do that because she wasn't certain this was true.

And even if it was, there was no guarantee he wouldn't kill John just for the pleasure of it. The power of it.

The light glinted off the Colt in Bill's hand. It seemed to strike her between the eyes, registering in her mind with myriad conflicting thoughts. One, he held the gun like an amateur. He may have killed, but he wasn't a weapons expert. Two, now that the moment of confrontation was finally at hand, now that he was standing over her, his gun trained on John, she found she didn't want a showdown.

She still wanted Bill out of her life once and for all, but now she wanted—*needed*—that future she'd never contemplated before. And with John.

She could almost imagine what John would say if she said her thoughts out loud. *"Your timing definitely needs some work, Kelsey."*

She had the despairing thought that now, through her own actions, she was about to lose everything she had only dreamed could exist.

She leaned back against the refrigerator. John still hadn't moved. How badly was he wounded? The scent of blood seemed all pervasive. Did that mean it was a mortal wound? Dear God, was he lying there not five feet from her, dying?

She bit her lip to keep a moan trapped inside. She knew better than to show any degree of emotion in front of Bill. She had learned that lesson the hard way; she'd lived with him.

"Don't get relaxed, Kelsey," Bill said. He chuckled. The sound sent shivers down her spine. "The game is just get-

ting fun. I'll tell you what, why don't both of you stand up.
You, too, lover boy."

Kelsey almost sobbed with relief as she saw John push to
his feet. He was wounded, his arm clung to his side, and a
large, dark stain already fanned out from his shoulder. But
it was high in the shoulder, away, far enough away from his
chest. He would live. If he had medical attention fairly
soon, that was.

Her imagination had painted an amazingly vivid picture
of that same stain in an alternate location. He rose slowly
and stood facing her, an intense message of some kind in his
eyes. Despairingly, she couldn't fathom his meaning.

"Okay, now, turn around. Not you, Kelsey, sweetheart.
Just lover boy."

John turned around, but not before sending another urgent message to her. God, what did he want her to do? Bill
had a gun trained on him, for pity's sake. Don't try to do
anything, she silently cautioned. You're already hurt,
please, *please* don't be a hero.

She knew what she had to do. She'd have to draw Bill's
attention away from John. She cleared her too dry throat.
"So" was all she managed to get out. What could she say to
him? How was prison? Still mad at me?

She wanted to giggle, and wondered briefly if the fear for
John, the fear of Bill, hadn't made her a few sandwiches shy
of a picnic. She ground her teeth together and held her
breath to keep from chuckling. She was hysterical, that was
it. That's all it was. Unfortunately, it didn't help her stop
thinking of possible things to say to Bill.

One of those questions finally sobered her completely.
Still want to carve me up into little pieces and feed me to
whatever dogs you can find?

"Is that all you have to say to me after all this time? Kelsey. Sweetheart. I'm disappointed. I have to tell you the
thought of hearing you screaming, begging for your life has
helped me fill many a long night in prison. A place, I might

add, that I didn't care for, didn't want to go to and never would have if you had been a good girl.''

''And died like you wanted me to?'' she asked. He would never know how terrified she was of him. She was strong now, yes, and even tough, but this was the man who had done so many horrible things to her that she had finally reached that point in her psyche where she had actually believed she'd deserved them. That there was something wrong with *her*.

She wasn't his victim any longer. But that knowledge didn't do anything to alleviate the fear of him. All she could hope to do was stall him. Stall the inevitable. Still, if she could salvage even a few minutes, those few minutes were life, and life was the most precious thing to her now. Because of John.

Bill looked her up and down, insultingly, leeringly. He eyed her with such a combination of longing, lust and control long gone haywire that she shrank back against the refrigerator instinctively.

She saw the quick flash of evil pleasure leap in his eyes. This was what he wanted, she thought. He wanted her scared, trembling. Would it buy her time, buy John time, if she gave him what he so obviously craved?

It wouldn't be hard to convince him, it wouldn't take a great deal of acting on her part. She was frightened to death.

John couldn't believe that this moment had finally arrived and had gone so dreadfully wrong. Just a moment earlier, watching Kelsey's saucy grin as she held out those silly rice things, he'd seen a glimpse of a proxy future, something different than that dreary beach-and-beer apartment with the TV on in the background.

For a single shimmering moment, caught up in her smile, snared by her wholly honest statement upstairs—*There are lots of ways to hide, John* and her other comment, *You got in, too*—he'd seen another life unfold. A life with Kelsey. A life filled with laughter, passion and joy. A life that could hold the kind of meaning he'd never dared even dream about. A life that actually embodied the essence of the word, a life that lent truth to words such as love, loyalty, faith. Trust.

He wished now that he hadn't hidden, wished he had given her those words, had let them reel out of that guarded part of him she had magically unlocked. He wished he had spelled out in graphic detail just what he felt for her, what she made him think, see, feel.

Because now, he might never have the chance. Now, in all likelihood, those words would remain unspoken, and they could both be killed with her never knowing that she had changed his very life. Had given life meaning.

He was standing there with his right arm of absolutely no use and he'd never been worth a damn with his left. His last chance had been stolen right from under his nose.

Pain was shooting through him and he could feel the slow, steady trickle of blood running down the inside of his sleeve. He could smell the sharp, coppery tang of it lingering in the air. He'd truly botched it.

He'd be damned if that was true. He'd be damned if Bill Winslow was going to waltz in here and steal dreams, hopes and futures away from him. An anger seized him, one so intense, so cold with hatred that it literally shook him. It swelled and magnified, infusing his veins with liquid fury.

No. He was going to have the chance to say those words to Kelsey. No psychopath of an ex-husband was going to stop him. He thought of Kelsey's original desire to kill Winslow, to wipe him from the face of the earth. And had to will himself to stay where he was, not to leap for him right now, yelling madly, terrifying the man every bit as much as he had ever terrified Kelsey.

"I don't think I would have found you quite this easily had it not been for your little friend who called in on the Laurie Winters show. Now there's someone I'd really like to meet. Not your friend, sweetheart, but that bitch who wouldn't tell me which city the call came from. Now that wasn't fair, was it?''

John wished he could see Kelsey's face, wished he could be near enough to her to know if she was all right, if Bill was crippling her with fear. He'd tried earlier to tell her, with his eyes only, that he wouldn't let Bill touch her. That he would give his life trying to keep him from her. But he wasn't certain she understood. How could she? Hadn't he steadfastly held her at a distance, emotionally if not physically?

But he hadn't been aloof, he wanted to tell her. He'd tried telling her, in his own strange way. "You got in," he'd told her. That was as much as he'd ever told anyone. Ever.

"How did you get in?" he asked Winslow. His voice sounded far away, tinny somehow. "Past the alarms?"

Winslow flicked him a contemptuous glance. "Oh, were those your Tinkertoys, Chandler?" He reached in his pocket and pulled out a roll of duct tape. "I got this from a pilot friend of mine. He'll never miss it." He chuckled and the sound made John's skin crawl. He wondered what the guys in the voice registration department would make of that laugh, it sounded unhinged to him.

"So, I just taped the window, right about where the alarm was. Piece of cake. I broke the glass, it didn't shatter, so your little toy only made a little noise. I pushed the little button, and voilà!" Winslow turned his burning gaze to Kelsey and falsettoed, "Honey, I'm home!"

John wanted to plant his fist, left or right, right in this smiling bastard's mouth. But he didn't dare, for fear the gun would go off and possibly hurt Kelsey, or even worse, take him out of the picture and leave her alone with this monster.

"You know, sweetheart, we never have talked about the past," Winslow said. "You're a hard lady to keep dead."

John remembered suddenly, in all-too-vivid detail, the accounts of her death in the newspaper, on the television news. He remembered that stupid tennis shoe that Charlie had insisted they plant at the scene. He thought of Kelsey's bare feet now. Was this to be the fate they had brought on themselves by displaying her death for all the world to see, to read about?

No, he swore silently. He wouldn't allow it. But how to gain the advantage? Winslow was obviously one step away from totally unravelling, but how to get him to cross that last step?

He took a small step forward, hoping against hope. He devoutly prayed that Winslow wasn't through bragging yet.

"Back off, lover boy. I'm not quite ready to shoot you. You haven't begged me to, yet. So, you get back there. Another step. And another. That's a good little agent."

John stepped backward until he felt Kelsey's body against his. Good. He felt better just touching her, being close enough that he could feel her warmth, smell her lemony scent.

Kelsey had nearly screamed aloud when John took a step forward, but realized as soon as his body touched hers, leaned into hers in some unspoken reassurance, that he'd planned it that way, he'd baited Bill into making him back away. She felt the first real glimmer of hope since she'd seen that dancing shadow on the stairs, had learned that John was still alive despite his shoulder wound.

"How cozy. Just the two of you. Moonlight and handguns. Quite the romantic couple. But your guns aren't doing much now, are they?"

It was typical of Bill, Kelsey thought, to have to display his awareness of detail, his knowledge, to demonstrate his control of a situation. But, she thought grimly, he wasn't dealing with the old Kelsey, the piteous woman who would grovel for mercy rather than stand up to him. And he didn't know John. She had the strong, clear sense that Bill was trying his tricks on the wrong man.

She could feel the tension building in John, and a quick glance to the side confirmed her suspicion. Gone was the tender lover of the night before. Gone was the confusion, the uncertainty when she'd asked him questions he'd rather not answer, questions about the future, about his emotions. And gone was the laughing partner, the easy friend. In the place of all that was a masterful agent, a total professional with a bad guy in his narrowed sights. Gun in his hand or not.

She still had one and could use it, too. The age-old question was, however, was she fast enough? Could she outdraw him? She couldn't take the risk—no matter how amateurish he looked holding that .45—that she could beat him to the trigger.

"You're making a mistake, Bill," she said. She could almost hear John willing her to continue. She did feel the slightest of pressures from his left arm, his good hand. Was he warning her to stop, or urging her forward?

She pressed on. "You see, it doesn't matter now. You're wanted from West Virginia to Texas. You'll never get free now."

She couldn't help shrinking against John at the sudden triumphant light that swept across Bill's features.

"But you don't understand, sweetheart. I *am* free. No one has ever been this free before. You see, always in the past, I had to play by the rules. Some of the rules. I never bruised your face, remember? I couldn't, you see, because people might have talked. But now, don't you get it? I don't have to play by anyone's rules but my own. That's true freedom. I can kill lover boy here, and no one can stop me."

Kelsey felt the truth of his words, insane though they were, saw it as he raised the gun to arm's length, pointed it at John's heart.

She couldn't say she would stop him, for Bill would just prove her wrong. John was there because of her, and could die for the same reason. She couldn't allow that to happen, no matter what happened to her.

"Is control all that important to you, Bill?" she asked. "Does destruction of something, someone, prove that you're better than they are? That makes you little more than a bully."

"Shut up, sweetheart. And don't try hiding behind Mr. Chandler now. And don't step in front of him. I'd just have to start with your kneecaps and work my way up. They tell me that's very, very painful. And I'd still kill him. You wouldn't want me to kill him so soon, would you?"

Think, Kelsey! she screamed at herself. *Think of something!*

John could almost feel Winslow's feral look of contempt and power lust. Poor old Pete inside that prison with Winslow all that time had hit the mark about the man; he was the human equivalent of a wolverine. This man killed for the pure pleasure of it. Kelsey was right. How could anyone have talked to this man and not seen the fact that he was certifiable? How could any review board have let him loose?

But Kelsey had given him a trump card in her questions to Bill, in her dismissing summation of her past abuse at this man's hands. Winslow was a bully. He might be a sociopath, as the psychiatrists at the trial said, or he might be that psychopath that Kelsey called him, but whatever anyone wanted to label him, the bottom line came down to the fact that he was a bully. Pure and simple.

And bullies were insecure.

Now, how to turn that basic, childlike insecurity into an ace without getting Kelsey murdered in the process?

He could think of only one way. And it would probably mean certain death for him. But at least he wouldn't go without her hearing those words that had been bottled up inside him for nearly a lifetime. And it would buy her time. She would have that chance she'd wanted, to finish things once and for all. He'd felt her gun still in her hand, felt it brush against his thigh. She could shoot him now, and with the FBI's blessing.

A strange gift, but a gift nonetheless.

Closing his eyes for a second in brief, utterly heartfelt prayer, he turned slowly, steadily, and completely ignoring Winslow, lifted his hands to Kelsey's face, ignoring the wrenching pain in his right shoulder, the blood on his fingers.

"What do you think you're doing?" Bill burst out.

Kelsey almost echoed Bill's outburst. She couldn't believe what John had just done. Couldn't believe he was facing her, hands upon her face, cupping them in urgent tenderness, a wild light flickering in the brown depths.

"I'm not hiding now, Kelsey. I can't. Just like I couldn't pretend the other night. I never pretended with you. I can't."

She felt as if some huge weight were being rolled from her. But why now? Was he so despairing, so convinced that they would die that he felt he had to say the words now? Let them be the last she ever heard?

"Get your hands off her," she heard Bill say, but she felt he was saying it from far away. She heard something else, too, a noise at the gate maybe. But it didn't seem important now, not with John's hands touching her, willing her to listen to him.

John's eyes bored into hers. "I told you that when I was a kid I was raised in an orphanage. That was true, but I wasn't an orphan. My parents put me there. They couldn't cope with having a kid and a life, too. I swore then—"

"Hey, what is this?"

John went on as if Bill hadn't spoken, repeating his words. "I swore then that I would never let myself in for that kind of hurt again. And I didn't."

"John..."

"Hey. You. Lover boy. You think I'm kidding? This isn't your show, you know? It's mine. Now get the hell away from her!"

"Not until now," John continued, as though he hadn't been interrupted. Kelsey could only stare at him wonderingly, marveling at him. "I was married, you know that. But I never let her inside. She never got through. You did. I meant what I said. And what you were saying earlier about futures . . . ?"

"I'll tell you about futures if you don't let go of her!" Bill screamed.

With John's hands on her face, with him saying the words she'd so longed to hear him speak, she wasn't afraid of Bill anymore. John's touch made Bill seem like a scorpion or a rattler . . . some poisonous creature that could be squashed.

"Yes?" she asked breathlessly. She leaned into him, ignoring Bill completely. She would rather die now than not hear this. This was life. It was all she'd ever wanted from life.

He turned slightly, blocking her view of Bill, keeping his hands on her face.

"Stop this! I'll shoot you right now. Do you hear me? I said stop it!" Bill yelled. He actually jumped up on both feet on his last command, a child furiously demanding the return of his toy.

"I want a future, Kelsey. With you."

John held her face, looked deep into her eyes, and realized he was saying every word he'd ever locked in his heart. This wasn't merely a ploy to make Winslow so angry he'd lose that thin hold on control. He was uttering all the things he'd wanted to be able to say every day for as long as he could remember.

He'd just never met the one woman he wanted to say them to. "Now I have you," he said, and meant it with all his heart.

More than ever before, he knew he had to get her out of this. For now, after telling her, he knew that they deserved a future together, that they were meant for each other. He couldn't begin to imagine a life without her. Before he'd thought it was enough to want her more than anything, but he realized now that it wasn't a matter of wanting that future with her, it was a matter of not being able to live without it.

He shifted another notch, blocking Winslow from her completely. He drew her even closer to him, willing her to understand, to believe.

Kelsey's heart seemed to have stopped beating. She'd nearly forgotten Bill in her longing to believe John's quiet words of love. But as he moved, understanding dawned. He hadn't been saying farewell, spilling every beautiful thought that lived in his soul, he was only working the moment, playing the lover, acting for Bill's sake, to throw him off guard.

He might as well have let Bill kill her. It would be easier to bear than knowing she'd clung to his every word, that his meaning had cleaved to her heart, her very soul, only to discover he'd been manipulating Bill into losing control.

"Do you trust me?" John asked.

Bill screamed for him to let her go. But he didn't fire.

She wanted to shake her head. How could she trust him when he was lying to her? Yet, because of the night before, because of the truth hidden in his words somewhere—even if he denied them later—she felt she had no choice.

"I trust you," she said. And to her surprise, she found she wasn't lying.

Winslow snapped. He lunged across the room, diving through the kitchen doorway with the roar of a bull and the force of a locomotive. Intent only on wresting Kelsey from John's embrace, he forgot that he held a gun.

John didn't.

At the same time that Winslow charged, John pitched Kelsey from him and lashed out sideways at Winslow's hand. The Colt fired again as it spun from Winslow's grasp.

As if in slow motion, John heard the gun's loud report and saw Kelsey falling to the Saltillo-tiled kitchen floor. For a moment time seemed to stop, then slowly run backward. He could hear his own voice saying all the things she'd freed in him, could feel the truth of those things echoing in his ears, in his heart.

She seemed to bounce on the floor, raise up for a moment, then drop again, her arms limp, her long, dark hair lifting almost playfully to dance in the air, only to fall again and lay still against her pale face.

Oddly, the scream of denial wasn't his own, it came from Winslow. He turned, wondering how this was possible that Winslow could be alive and Kelsey downed.

His yell of rage, of pure unadulterated hatred made Winslow drop to a crouch and back away suddenly. He leapt, lunging for the man, nothing on his mind but Kelsey's inert form and the sharp clarity of knowing that, finally, even if it was too late for everything important in life, Winslow was going to pay.

Kelsey heard the twin screams, recognized both voices and the nuances behind each one. Bill was furious because nothing was going according to plan. But in John's cry she heard the echo of what he'd been telling her earlier, and the sharp echo of what *she* had felt earlier. He believed her dead.

She wasn't dead. She needed to tell him that, but couldn't think how with all the noise. She was only grazed on her left upper arm. It hurt, but not very much. Something between a bee sting and a burn. A very bad burn, she thought giddily. Her head hurt more from having slammed into the tile.

Her vision blurred, but cleared with her next thought. John. He thought she'd been shot. His scream, his yell, was one of pure vengeance. He was going to kill Winslow . . . for *her*.

She pushed herself unsteadily to her knees, groping for the bar, fumbling to retrieve her .38 from the floor. She found it. It felt foreign in her hand.

She could see the two men slamming into each other with absolute killing hatred. She was momentarily sickened, not, oddly enough, at the sheer brutality, but because her age-old wish was about to come true. John was going to kill Bill. Because of her, he wasn't waiting for the troops to rush in, wasn't fighting Winslow by the rules. He wanted Winslow dead. For her.

She had to stop it.

She had practiced firing at a moving target a thousand times, was an expert marksman with the .38. But now, with Winslow in her sights, she found her hands were shaking, her knees were trembling. And Bill had nothing to do with it.

She couldn't shoot because she was afraid, dreadfully afraid she would miss and accidentally hit John. One sudden shift, one wrong turn, one trembling hand and she could kill the one man who made life worth living, the one man who made her understand that extreme justice only bred extreme injustice.

Without a second thought, she raised her hands and fired the gun at the ceiling. Both men flinched and rolled aside to face her, Bill screaming something at her, John staring at her as though she were a ghost, in mingled fear and wild hope.

She felt cold and hot at the same time, and mindless. She didn't so much as hesitate. She shot across the floor as though propelled by jet fuel and dropped to a protective crouch beside Bill. Completely ignoring John, she held the squat gun barrel to Bill's temple.

"It's over," she said, meaning it absolutely. *"It is over, forever."*

Her hand trembled with her hatred of him, her past fear of him. He'd caused her so much pain, so much anguish, and now her moment, the moment she'd worked for, trained for some three long years, was finally at hand. And the worst thing he'd ever done to her was let her think John was dead, was make John believe she was. The moment was at hand, all right. *Her* hand.

Suddenly she could remember every time he'd struck her, every time he'd humiliated her, clearly recalled, in stark detail, an afternoon when four FBI agents had come knocking at her door to tell her that he'd put out a contract on her, that her husband wanted her dead. And she could remember—still felt it—that gut-wrenching despair when she'd thought he'd killed John.

Could she kill him? Could she pull that trigger?

Yes. Yes, she could. Somebody had to. Her finger curled around the narrow strip of metal. It fit her finger exactly, funny how she'd never noticed that. It felt so right. Yes, she knew she could pull the trigger. She knew she could end it right now. Forever. She'd never wanted anything more.

But that wasn't true, was it?

She did want something more than she wanted Bill dead. She wanted far more than that.

Her hand was trembling with fear and her heart was pounding too rapidly, too erratically. But the trembling wasn't caused by Bill Winslow, and her heart beat not in hatred, not in bloodlust, but with love for someone else.

John had watched her dazzlingly swift action with awe. He'd no sooner heard the shot than she'd whipped across the kitchen to press the gun to Winslow's temple. He saw the hatred on her face, the long suppressed moment of revenge making her hands tremble, her face white.

He wanted to tell her to just do it. He'd stand by her; hell, he'd even claim he did it, or that she'd had to do it in self-defence. It wouldn't even get to court, he'd see to that. Any D.A. would believe him.

He heard the front gate shatter, heard the frantic pounding on the front door. If you're going to do it, honey, he begged, do it *now*. While I can still help you, while I can still do something about it.

Slowly, her sultry voice marred with emotion, Kelsey started speaking. "I . . . love . . . you . . . John. I . . . love you far . . . more than . . . I hate this . . . man," she said. She sounded drugged, as though she were fighting to get each word out of her mouth.

John felt his heart stop. He looked up from the gun to see her face, to see if he could read the truth there. She was staring at Winslow, but her lips were curving slightly, a soft, beautiful smile touching them.

Tears sprang to his eyes at her decision, at her amazing struggle with one of the hardest, most difficult things to let go of in life—hatred. She'd said she loved him more. There was no greater testament than that.

Winslow had said earlier that not playing by the rules made him free. He was dead wrong. Love from a woman like Kelsey made a man free. Gave him everything on earth, and more.

"It's over," John said. "It's finally over."

John pulled himself up, stood groggily beside her. He looked down at Bill Winslow's confused, whey-colored face, and to Kelsey's calm, almost serene stance. He had admired her before, had been angry with her, had conceded to her, had held her in his arms in glorious passion. But he'd never been so proud of her as he was now.

"You are undoubtedly the most remarkable woman," he said.

"I thought I was a menace."

"That, too."

Winslow murmured something. Kelsey just pressed the gun barrel deeper into his temple. He was immediately silent.

"Would you open my door before they knock it down, too?" she asked.

The front door crashed open and a full regalia of armed men stormed the room. They took in the situation at a glance, and everyone froze.

"Too late," she said.

John grinned and waved his teams forward.

As they cautiously approached Winslow, John said, "If there's anything you've proven to me in the past few days, Kelsey, it's that it's never too late."

He placed his left hand beneath her good shoulder and helped her to her feet.

She smiled up at him. "Is that an offer?" she asked. "Now, don't give me one of those no-yes answers. Don't even stop and think about it. Remember, I have a gun...."

Monday, November 29
10:00 a.m., Lubbock, Texas

"We look like we're on a peace march," Kelsey said, tracing her finger along John's white, medical arm band.

"We'd cancel each other out politically...I'm right, you're left."

She looked over at the tray of goodies he'd brought up to their room. "There's nothing left there, either."

John groaned and pulled her over to him. She settled on his chest in a now familiar position, placed an elbow on either side of his head, and winced as the bandage around her arm pulled in protest.

"When did the doctor say yours would be off?" he asked.

"Day after tomorrow," she said.

"And mine a week later."

She made a curtain of her hair and framed his face. It could have been night.

"Are you going to keep your hair dark?" he asked.

She smiled and tossed it over her shoulder, letting the sun back in. "I don't know. I rather like it."

"So do I," he said, but she could have green hair for all he cared. As long as she was with him. As long as he could run his hands through that silken mass and feel it spilling over his body.

She cocked her head slightly and smiled, but her eyes were serious.

"What?" he asked.

"It's time to talk about tomorrow," she said.

"Are we going somewhere?"

Her smile broadened and a flicker of it met her gaze. John was sure he'd never been so happy. He ran his hands down her back, loving the feel of her satin skin. He grinned up at her, tickling her a little. She squirmed against him and to his own surprise he found himself responding.

"There isn't going to be any tomorrow if we keep this up," he said. "I'll be a dead man."

"You love it," she said knowingly.

"I do." He leered.

"And you love me," she announced.

"Yes," he agreed. He wondered at the admission ever having been difficult. It was so very, very easy when that love was returned, when it was constantly, joyously enticed from him.

"And I love you. The thing is, I can't stay in Lubbock, Texas, while you live in D.C.," she said.

"That would be problematic," he said. He pretended to give it hard thought. "It would be a long time between dates."

She smiled, but a shadow had crept into her eyes. He couldn't bear to see it. Not in Kelsey's eyes.

"I've been giving this a lot of thought," he said. And he had. "And I see it this way, you could join the Bureau—you're better than most of the folks they hire—and we could go out on team assignments."

She grinned, the shadow fading from those glorious blue eyes. God, how he loved her.

"Or," he said, "I could quit the Bureau and we could start a private detective agency—Chandler and Chandler immediately comes to mind—and we could hire out for comic relief."

She continued to smile, but John could still detect the shadow.

"Or," he said, trying not to laugh, "we could join the circus. I'm sure there's a real need for the Chandlers' amazing rice cake routine."

She chuckled, but didn't answer. A bad sign, he thought, and reveled in knowing that, in understanding her so well, he could read her moods, knew the telltale signs of her joy, her passion, her discomfort.

"Seriously, Kelsey, I don't really care where we are or what we do. I want you to be with me forever. Married. White picket fence. Nash Rambler in the driveway—"

"A Nash Rambler?" she asked with a chuckle, the shadow gone completely now.

"Well, if I quit, and you quit, it'll be about the only thing we can afford. I'll bet, if we ask, Mrs. Stedman has one in her garage. *But,*" he added before she could pipe in, "there's another solution altogether. Why don't we get married, you move to D.C., I'll take the Washington beat, and you do your seminars and training classes in a city with about a hundred thousand more clients."

"It was the being with you forever part I was after," she said. "The logistics can wait."

It was his turn to chuckle.

"Are we going to watch the news today?" she asked.

"Don't we always?"

"Let's don't," she said. And he knew why; the courts in three states were handing down their decisions on Bill Winslow today.

"Don't you want to know?" he asked.

She shook her head. "West Virginia's already basically said it's the death penalty. Texas is calling for one, too. Colorado is going to go for life. His attorney is going for insanity. Let them haggle over Bill Winslow's hide. I don't care. For me, it's over."

She sighed, looked thoughtful, then smiled at him with such warmth, such tenderness, it took his breath away. "It's over and done with."

"No, it isn't," he said, running his hands up her sides, tracing the soft swell of her breast pressing against him. "It's not over by a long shot."

He raised her up slightly, holding her above him, taking an already stiff nipple into his mouth.

She arched her back to meet his hot mouth, to allow him to suckle, to flick her with his teeth, his lips, his tongue. Sharp, jagged streaks of sensation shot through her, firing her anew, rekindling a flame she'd believed so thoroughly banked it might not bear heat again for days. But she could never get enough of John. Never.

She swung her legs around him, straddling him, riding him as he replaced mouth and tongue with hands and fingers. She sat up straight, resting lightly over him, feeling him grow beneath her.

She ran her hands through the brown crisp curls on his chest, lightly strafing his small nipples with her nails, bringing them to taut points. He moaned softly and raised his hips. She rubbed against him and he moaned louder.

Smiling, she knelt over him, kissing first his mouth, then his neck, the hollows in his collarbone, the muscled chest. His hands swept down her back, teasing her, imploring her. He moved his hands lower, cupping her buttocks, lifting her slightly, molding her to his grip, kneading, exhorting her to take him.

She resisted, though her entire body felt limp with the ache to feel him inside her once again. This time was her time. He'd given her so very much. She wanted to return his regard a thousandfold.

His skin felt soft and supple, she thought, his muscles rippling beneath her touch. And he smelled of her and of him, of a thousand memories of the days before, the nights in between. She drank it in like the finest of wines.

When he would have rolled over, she spread his arms out to the side, telling him he couldn't move, that he was bound, by honor if nothing else, to remain where he was. This was her turn for exploration, for discovery.

And she delighted in every moan, every groan, and each small tensing or stretching to meet her tongue, her hands, her questing touch.

"I can't take this," he said.

"You have to," she replied, smiling, but feeling she couldn't take much more, either.

His hands lifted from the bed suddenly, capturing her, stopping her. He rolled her onto her back and pinned her against the bed. He swept her hands above her head and held them with one of his.

"Your arm's getting better," she said.

"Watch me," he answered.

She chuckled, then gasped as he bent over her and took a turgid nipple into his mouth. Still keeping her pinned, his hands stroked her from her wrists to her knees, lightly then firmly, and then so delicately that she shivered in reflexive response. He nipped her like a stallion and allowed his tongue free rein.

She murmured his name, writhing beneath him, arching up to him, aching for him, begging for him. And still he wouldn't stop.

His fingers found the hot, wet core of her and slid inside, dancing a rhythm that made her shudder, made her arch to take him in. His mouth plundered hers, and gently, roughly, took her breasts, one then the other, playing no favorites.

And still he held her hands far above her head while his tongue traveled lower, tracing the dip of her waist, the swell of her stomach, the sensitive apex of her thighs. He flicked his tongue across her swollen and eager core, keeping his fingers where they were, moving them faster and faster.

His hand released hers and slid sensually down her arm, across her shoulders and to her breasts. Touching her in all places, demanding she give him everything she had to give, he encouraged that rare trust, that beauty only he could inspire.

She called his name and arched even higher.

And he stopped abruptly. She opened her eyes, nearly stunned senseless by his onslaught, by his sudden cessation.

"Are you going to marry me? And don't give me one of your it's-cereal-for-you answers. Now, as you can no doubt see . . . *I* have the gun."

He hovered over her for a moment, his weaponry obvious. She chuckled and opened herself to him.

"You're going to have to use it," she said.

"You're a very tough lady," he said, smiling as he slipped inside her.

She cupped his face with both hands. "Oh, yes, John," she said.

"Is that your answer?"

"It is."

"I suppose shaking on the deal would be a moot point, now," he said.

"Oh, I'm shaking," she said.

He chuckled, but very soon, he was shaking, too.

It was only just.

* * * * *

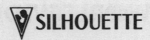

Cruel Legacy

One man's untimely death deprives a wife of her husband, robs a man of his job and offers someone else the chance of a lifetime...

Suicide — the only way out for Andrew Ryecart, facing crippling debt. An end to his troubles, but for those he leaves behind the problems are just beginning, as the repercussions of this most desperate of acts reach out and touch the lives of six different people — changing them forever.

Special large-format paperback edition

OCTOBER
£8.99

WORLDWIDE

Have a romantic Christmas with Silhouette

Three new Sensation novels that feature the love and passions at Christmas time are contained in this attractive gift pack.

A Christmas Marriage
Dallas Schulze

❧

A Country Christmas
Jackie Weger

❧

A Cowboy for Christmas
Anne McAllister

PUBLISHED NOVEMBER 1994   PRICED £5.85

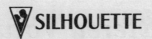

▼ **SILHOUETTE**

Available from WH Smith, John Menzies, Volume One, Forbuoys, Martins, Woolworths, Tesco, Asda, Safeway and other paperback stockists.

▼ SILHOUETTE

Sensation

COMING NEXT MONTH

FIREBRAND
Paula Detmer Riggs

He Who Dares

Years ago Judd Calhoun had accidentally started a fire, with disastrous consequences. Now he was back in the same town as a fire chief—and he was desperate to see something other than hatred burning in Darcy's eyes...

MISS EMMALINE AND THE ARCHANGEL
Rachel Lee

Under Blue Wyoming Skies

Someone was watching her. Emma knew that something bad was going to happen again. And then Gage Dalton walked into her life. He was dangerous and unpredictable...yet he was the only man who made her feel safe and whole.